JULY

S	M	T	W	T	F	S
1	2	3	4	5	6	7
8	9	10	11	12	13	14
15	16	17	18	19	20	21
22	23	24	25	26	27	28
29	30	31				

AUGUST

S	M	T	W	T	F	S
			1	2	3	4
5	6	7	8	9	10	11
12	13	14	15	16	17	18
19	20	21	22	23	24	25
26	27	28	29	30		

SEPTEMBER

S	M	T	W	T	F	S
					1	2
3	4	5	6	7	8	9
10	11	12	13	14	15	16
17	18	19	20	21	22	23
24	25	26	27	28	29	30

OCTOBER

S	M	T	W	T	F	S
1	2	3	4	5	6	7
8	9	10	11	12	13	14
15	16	17	18	19	20	21
22	23	24	25	26	27	28
29	30	31				

NOVEMBER

S	M	T	W	T	F	S
			1	2	3	4
5	6	7	8	9	10	11
12	13	14	15	16	17	18
19	20	21	22	23	24	25
26	27	28	29	30		

DECEMBER

S	M	T	W	T	F	S
					1	2
	5	6	7	8	9	16
	12	13	14	15	16	
	19	20	21	22	23	
	26	27	28	29	30	W

world holiday)—equals December 31 and follows December 30 every

Wtd

OF TIME AND THE CALENDAR

BY ELISABETH ACHELIS

The World Calendar 1937
The Calendar for Everybody 1943

OF TIME
AND
THE CALENDAR

ELISABETH ACHELIS

HERMITAGE HOUSE
NEW YORK, 1955

FOR THE MANY
WHO BELIEVE IN AND ARE WORKING FOR
A BETTER WORLD

"Time that 'takes survey of all the world' should itself be one and the same for all the world."

Editorial in *New York Times*

"Our stability is but balance. . . ."

Robert Bridges

"The World Calendar appears to be an enormous improvement . . . I approve heartily of the change and hope it may be carried into effect."

James Truslow Adams

"I am sufficiently informed about the history and the arguments to line myself before the public upon the side of the proposals of The World Calendar Association."

Robert A. Millikan

"I am with you calendar wise."

Carrie Chapman Catt

CONTENTS

OF TIME AND THE CALENDAR

FOREWORD

A review of the past
A survey of the present
A plan for the future
In the process of acceptance

THE CALENDAR and the clock.

Have you ever wondered at the curious inconsistency between these two ingenious and fascinating devices for reckoning the flow of Time? The calendar measures our yeartime and the clock records our daytime, yet, in spite of their common purpose, these two indispensable timekeepers are never in harmony with each other.

The clock is a simple, precise, scientific instrument that moves as regularly as the earth rotates on its axis—24 hours to the day, 60 minutes to the hour, 60 seconds to the minute.

The calendar—even after several revisions since it was first developed in ancient Egyptian Dynasties—still remains a complicated and fickle timepiece, at best loosely suggesting the solar length of the years, seasons, months, weeks and days and, at worst, replete with caprice and quirks, lacking order and reliability. In addition to the Gregorian calendar—the one most widely in use throughout the world today—there are many others (in India, for example, some thirty) to add to the confusion of our time recording.

11

This small book recounts the complexities and confusions in the present calendar, recalls its origin in remote history, traces its development in diverse civilizations, and points to its limitless potentialities for effective service through the simple revisions proposed in The World Calendar.

The World Calendar develops the present calendar into a scientific, civil instrument for measuring and recording the flow of time in an ordered manner. It is a stabilizer of our days and years in perpetuity, a harbinger of peace and good will.

Just as The World Calendar brings rhythm—variety in unity—into our daily affairs and lives, so also will it help our present confused world to evolve into one harmonious whole.

I

"A SMOOTH AND SUBTLE THIEF"

Thirty dayes hath Nouember,
Aprill, June, and September,
February hath xxviii alone,
And all the rest have xxxi.

—Richard Grafton, *Chronicles of England* (1562)

THE GREGORIAN CALENDAR has proved useful in calendar evolution, but now in our modern world it has become a confusing and costly timepiece wherein nothing fits, nothing agrees, nothing is stable. No year follows another in any consistent pattern; indeed, fourteen varieties of years and twenty-eight types of months succeed each other in bewildering procession. With the past, present and future years beginning on different days of the week, days and dates never agree from year to year. Months range from 28 to 31 days in length and contain either four or five Sundays, Mondays, Tuesdays, continuing in this erratic manner throughout the week. Likewise quarter years and half years are unequal: the first quarter year contains 90 or 91 days (depending on a common or a leap year), the second quarter contains 91 days and the third and fourth quarters each contain 92 days; the first half year thus has 181 or 182 days and the second half 184 days. A year of 52 1/7 weeks has either 53 Sundays, Mondays, Tuesdays, Wednesdays, Thursdays, Fridays or Saturdays.

One of history's inexplicable mysteries is man's toleration of this irresponsible situation for more than 2,000 years! We smile indulgently at the primitive prejudices of ancient cultures, their fear of the new, their stolid adherence to the old. Yet, in many respects, man basically is still the same obdurate creature he was centuries ago.

Picture for a moment the present temperamental calendar family with which we must daily cope.

The *Day-child*—the confused one—neither knows where it belongs nor how many days it has for play or work within the months. The *Week-child*—the unruly one—runs in and out of the calendar as it pleases, wholly unconcerned by the effect of its petulance upon calendar's family life. The *Month-child*—the neglected one—has no room of its own: sometimes it is given the smallest room, as in February (28 days); sometimes a larger room, as in April (30 days); and sometimes the largest room, as in March (31 days). The *Quarter-year-child* and the *Half-year-child*—the bewildered ones—like *Alice in Wonderland* expand and contract without rhyme or reason.

The obvious result of this temperamental situation—this lack of plan and discipline—is chaos and cost, frustration and unhappiness.

A noted business man has described the present calendar as "a smooth and subtle thief," robbing us not only of time and money but also of tranquility of mind.

A few specific examples, drawn from research studies published during the past twenty-five years in the *Journal of Calendar Reform* (the official publication of The

World Calendar Association), will illustrate this description and point up the incredible conditions confronting us as we struggle with the present bizarre calendar.

Some years ago a well-known radio commentator estimated that our present system of reckoning time costs the City of New York approximately $5,322,886.25 annually, devouring the taxpayer's dollar at the rate of $607 per hour. He arrived at these staggering figures by asking a simple question:

"What day falls on the 18th of next month?

"How long has it taken you to arrive at the correct answer? Unless you have a calendar within reach or your wife's birthday happens to fall on that date, I defy you to give an immediate answer. Instead you say: 'This being the 12th, let me see, 30 days has September, April, June, etc. That gives us 31 days—humm—this is Sunday —next Sunday would be the 19th—the following Sunday the 26th—humm—the first falls on Tuesday—8th—15th— hum-m-m—22nd—minus four—Oh yes, the 18th would be a—Friday.'

"In terms of radio copy these lines would consume 30 seconds of air time. Give the average person one minute to do the problem. Assume that half the population of New York alone worked at it once a day—58,333 hours daily, or 7,291 working days, or 26 years of work for one man. At 25 cents an hour [this minimum was several years ago!] he would receive $14,583.25. This for one day's cerebration in one city of the U.S.A. The annual bill would be well over five million dollars."

Our radio commentator was particularly conscious of this enormous waste because, as he pointed out, commentators frequently find it necessary to compute the day of a certain date while they are on the air, and network at that time cost about $2,700, exclusive of talent and production costs, for fifteen minutes!

Take the sad story of small business as it struggles to cope with our antiquated calendar. Not long ago a small-town drugstore estimated calendar fluctuations wiped out two weeks' profit; a small lumber mill found it negotiated a 90-day contract at no profit whatever; a food store estimated spoilage due to calender uncertainties cost it 10 per cent loss on its vegetable profit; an assembling plant paid 18 per cent overtime charges; a small paper mill suffered 8.4 per cent over the absenteeism in six months; a small dry goods store ran a loss on three different sales; and a local trucker found his total pay roll upped 23 per cent overtime on long week-ends.

Under the present calendar, with its variant weekdays for *date* holidays, such as the Fourth of July, or its variant dates for *day* holidays, such as Labor Day, there is practically no way for small business to anticipate or estimate its holiday business except by guesswork. There is no basis for comparison. Perhaps last year a holiday fell on a Friday or Saturday, simultaneously with weekly and mid-month pay days, but the following year it falls two days off, affecting the expenditures and vacationing habits of everybody. Then, too, there is the glaring defect that months may have four or five Tuesdays or Thursdays and again four or five Saturdays and Sundays, not to mention the exasperating differences of 24, 25, 26 or 27 weekdays in the months.

The difficulties of 53 Sundays, Mondays, etc., are complicated. To every American citizen the payment of income taxes on a 53rd Friday causes real hardship because

53 payments do not mean a full 53 weeks' payment. Assuming that one continues to work and to remain in the same income bracket, this inequity is taken care of in the following year but not without much time-consuming calculation.

So important is calendar fluctuation to big business that one department store employs three people whose entire work is researching and mathematically adjusting comparative holiday and date figures from preceding years. One railroad has an entire division of its traffic department occupied with similar comparisons. And one of the most hectic and important departments of a chain grocery store is the one correlating the work between traffic and buying departments. A shipment needed on a Tuesday morning is a loss proposition if it arrives on a Monday holiday and requires overtime charges for delivery and storage; and spoilables shipped in for the week-end are no good if Friday is a holiday and half the people are away.

Big business meets the situation at considerable cost with expert research, and even then occasionally goes for a tumble. Small business has no experts and cannot afford individual calculating service. The avoidable variations of the calendar produce losses as ridiculous and exasperating as would be caused by the variations of the universal use of changeable clocks.

Clyde Mann, former managing director of the Certified Building Registry of the United States, has this to say of the business problem: "Another spot where calendar irregularity has a baneful influence is in payment of rents, interest, insurance and contractors' bills. Unequal lengths of months and quarters cause definite losses, some trifling in themselves, but enormous in their aggregate. The lack of a fixed relationship between weekdays and month-days means payments frequently retarded two to four days, and the interest charges piled up by this aggregate of oft-repeated delays amount to many millions annually. Payments fluctuate similarly around legal holidays.

"Now this financial 'lag' may seem a small matter," Mr. Mann continues. "It is a financing cost that has long been accepted as inevitable in the machinery of mortgage and management. Yet it would be greatly abated under the proposed new calendar. And remember, it is one of the factors that helps discourage private capital from venturing into the building field.

"There are listed 49,000 industrial plants which find their market in the building field. I venture to predict that each one of them would find some definite benefit from the proposed revision of the calendar."

The Canadian Bureau of Statistics, which receives reports from 205 retail establishments, states that no less than 35 of the Dominion's larger stores are employing a four-week or a five-week month in their accounting departments. This is alleged to eliminate errors that crop up when comparisons are made between months in different years which happen to have an unequal number of weekdays.

An example of the error in calculation that the irregular calendar can produce in this sober and steady world of statistics is also provided by the Canadian Bureau. It concerns the report of a large power company. In January, 1936, it produced 220 million kilowatt hours as compared to 258 million kilowatt hours during January,

1937. Offhand, you would say that the calculation of the increase was a simple exercise in arithmetic—an increase of 17.3 per cent. But when we look deeper into the report, we discover that January, 1937, had an *extra* Saturday and Sunday, on which days the output is naturally less than on weekdays, 30 per cent less for Saturday, 75 per cent for Sunday. Making allowance for the extra week-end, we find the rate of increase becomes 21.5 instead of 17.3 per cent.

A few years ago an independent study of the effects of the present calendar on American business was conducted through the Controllers Institute of America. The questionnaire listed twelve of the major difficulties in scheduling sales or production reported by businessmen due to the calendar. These included: variations in the number of weekdays per month, "grasshopper dates" interfering with schedules, variable wage costs for workers paid on a weekly or monthly basis, salesmen's expenses due to "lay-overs" on midweek holidays, losses resulting from ill-timed advertising because of calendar variations, and other factors.

Replies to this questionnaire came from 538 controllers, working for companies with a total capitalization of more than 20 billion dollars—a sizable cross section of U. S. industry. More than 86 per cent—an overwhelming majority—indicated that the present calendar created difficulties and added expenses for them.

It was impossible to estimate the total costs incurred by these companies due to defects in the calendar—but the costs undoubtedly ran into many millions of dollars each year.

Of the 466 industrialists indicating difficulties with the

present calendar, 437 or 93.8 per cent indicated that a stabilized calendar would alleviate these difficulties.

In 1952, a survey of labor absenteeism due to wandering holidays under the present calendar indicated that working people would lose a total of $461,723,328 in the United States during that year.

This figure was reached by computing the number of working days lost and multiplying the number of days by the average daily wage then being paid in U. S. industries.

Another estimate of the monetary loss from wandering holidays has been made by a noted industrial economist, Joseph M. Naab. Mr. Naab said:

"Take just one small unit of calendar expense under our present system, namely, the effect of midweek holidays on business and industry. From my own practical experience in the operation of controlled production . . . I estimate that as much as 1.5 per cent loss may result in a period of one year, due to starts and stops in the even flow of production and distribution. Most of this loss would be saved under a stable and consistent calendar. If a 1.5 per cent loss is charged against the national product of 300 to 350 billion dollars, you will get from this item alone a saving almost equal to the present interest charge on the national debt."

Mr. Naab indicated that the cost of such losses under the present calendar came to a total between 4.5 and 5.25 billion dollars.

It is easy to see why leading educators favor The World Calendar. Schools and colleges have tight budgets and cannot afford the millions spent every year in preparing new schedules for classes and examinations.

Eventually these added costs have to be paid by parents and school benefactors—the schools must obtain funds, through taxes or tuition, through higher fees or the gifts of philanthropists.

The making of new schedules year after year, forced upon school administrators by the present calendar, is a waste of money without any possible justification.

Successful farming—whether it is cattle-raising, truck gardening, or tobacco growing; whether it has to do with dairy herds, fruits or staples—calls for exact measurements of time, careful bookkeeping, and statistics that are comparable year by year, month by month, week by week.

Scientific methods are making the farmer, the stockman and the horticulturist as eager for a balanced calendar as any businessman. Farmers go in for crop-rotation plans of three to four years' duration—and they need accurate dependable ways of keeping track of their planting and harvesting.

The present calendar, with its variations from year to year, costs farmers money by forcing them to do additional bookkeeping and constant re-scheduling of crop planting.

Lawyers have to bear in mind the time within which clients must pay property, inheritance, income and franchise taxes; the time when the principal and interest payments on mortgages must be met; the time when patent applications must be filed in the U. S. or other countries; the time when claims against the estates of deceased persons must be filed; the time of court trials—and other occasions for which they must refer to the calendar.

Every department of the U. S. government and of the

governments of many other countries has encountered the defects of the present calendar. According to a high official in the Bureau of Efficiency, specific examples of shocking calendar errors in existing government statistics may be found in practically every federal department. Many legislative and executive officials have gone on record in favor of a more sensible system.

In the United States, for example, the Department of Labor has the task of keeping careful tabulations on employment and industrial turnover; the Department of Commerce keeps statistics on domestic and foreign trade; the Department of Agriculture prepares data on farm production and marketing trends.

All these data are inevitably affected by seasonal variations. To chart trends based upon comparisons between various years is a tedious and inaccurate job when the lengths of the quarters vary and the number of Saturdays in the months fluctuates so greatly.

The work of every government department in every country of the globe would be expedited and streamlined by adoption of The World Calendar.

The savings to taxpayers would be large in every nation.

No one escapes the harassments of the present calendar—not even the housewife. Mrs. Catherine Jackson Alger, whose father, an ardent calendar revisionist, was President of the American Academy of Arts and Sciences, stated the case for the homemaker this way:

"Not as an expert nor as a member of any unusual profession, but as one of innumerable housewives and mothers, I wish to make my lay comment on the proposed World Calendar. This calendar, with its orderly arrangement and predictable holidays, appeals to me as a piece of good housekeeping that the civilized world should carry out without further delay. . . .

"With the proposed World Calendar we could arrange family holidays together, as now we are not often able to do; we could plan ahead both our personal and group activities more clearly than now. How astonishing it seems that now we should positively require the aid of a calendar to make any engagement more than a week ahead. No one can make a business or personal date for the 17th of next month until she finds out whether that is Sunday or Monday. We are so used to this waste of time and words that we do not appreciate the easy simplicity of knowing, for instance, that the 17th of a particular month is always a fixed day of the week. . . . The mother of a family particularly should appreciate the new calendar, with all her problems of school days, business engagements, neighborhood clubs, children's parties, and conflicting holidays to plan for."

In these few examples, which can be multiplied many times, is there not revealed perhaps a psychological reason, an underlying cause, which explains in part the confusion, insecurity, planlessness and perplexities that face us in our world today? Is it not reasonable to assume that the present discordant calendar, used by so many peoples and in all international relationships and transactions, may not exert its baneful influence in other directions as well? As a man thinketh so is he. How can nations, governments, leaders and peoples hope for peace, harmony, cooperation and good will when they are daily using a time system diametrically opposing these hopes and ideals?

The first step for civilization is to bring order, discipline and rhythm into the temperamental calendar family, and to develop and accept without further delay a harmonious calendar family that will represent everything we esteem. This is an obligation of every government and citizen of the world. Such a forward step will bring closer, much closer, our aspirations for cooperation, good will and greater peace. Our days will be lived in greater stability and harmony. Our vast potentialities for increased progress, yet unrevealed and unknown, will unfold before us. We need only to recall the vast benefits Standard Clock Time brought to our daily lives, to our transportation and communication systems, and to our economic and social activities. Certainly a happy calendar family will help to create a happier human family.

Before discussing the purpose of an improved time plan, we turn to the ever-fascinating story of the calendar. A review of its history will help to explain the urgent need for the revision embodied in The World Calendar—the plan now before the United Nations.

II

OCEAN OF YEARS

A wonderful stream is the River Time,
With a faultless rhythm and a musical rhyme,
And a broader sweep, and a surge sublime,
As it blends with the Ocean of Years.

—B. F. Taylor

PRIMITIVE MAN'S first efforts at measurement dealt with his need for recording the passage of days. The attempt to formulate a calendar was his earliest organized achievement. From this beginning he progressed to measure other things—length, height, weight and distance. The arts of writing, architecture and mathematics were inevitable results of the calendar.

Calendars came long before clocks. Measurement of days into convenient bundles—such as weeks, months, seasons and years—was more important than the counting of hours, minutes and seconds. The cave man felt no need for hourglass or sundial. Clocks, as precise measures of Time, did not come into use until the thirteenth century. Meanwhile the quest for calendar improvement had been going on for thousands of years.

Creating a good calendar was a baffling problem. Many ingenious experiments were attempted. The difficulty was always how to establish an accurate and harmonious relationship between the various natural time markers provided by the sun, moon and stars. Perfecting the calendar was an arduous process that has continued through the ages and is still with us.

Ancient Babylonians and Egyptians, Julius Caesar and Pope Gregory XIII were all pioneers in devising a better time system. Upon their endeavors rests the calendar now used by the Western world. To a certain extent it has also been accepted by Eastern nations, which use it alongside such diverse systems as those of the Jews, the Moslems and the peoples of India.

The Caesar-Gregory calendar is far from perfect. It still contains annoying irregularities and inherited inconveniences which demand correction—especially in an age when men are living closer together and when their many interrelated activities call for a high level of accuracy, order and stability.

Proposed improvements have been a matter of international concern from the beginning of this century. Demand for their enactment came first from the International Chamber of Commerce in 1910; the movement was making progress when World War I interfered. It was further advanced by the League of Nations from 1923 until 1939 when World War II interrupted. It came before the United Nations in 1947, when Secretary-General Trygve Lie made a comprehensive report providing the basis for legislative proposals in 1949 and 1953.

In the latter year, the initiative came from India, whose motion, supported by a Council vote of 12 to 2, stated: "The Government of India consider that the plan for the reform of the Gregorian Calendar proposed by The World Calendar Association is of great importance to the nations of the world. The purpose of the plan is to adopt for the whole world . . . a new, fixed, uniform and invariable calendar . . . more regular, scientific and advantageous than the Gregorian."

An accompanying Memorandum added: "The ideal of the whole world is to have a logical and perpetual calendar to replace the present Gregorian Calendar because it is widely recognized that the calendar we now use is unsatisfactory for the economic, social, educational, scientific and other activities of man. Modern progress demands the change. Such a revision has been the subject of study and research on the part of experts, institutions and international organizations for many years. The consensus of opinion is that a new time system is necessary . . . that it should be uniform, an invariable calendar, perpetually the same."

Thus calendar reform became an urgent matter for international action in 1954.

The objective is to establish a single standard civil calendar for the entire world, a scientific system of time measurement, without sectional, racial or sectarian influence. The improvements required are that the new calendar should adjust the irregular length of months, should equalize the quarterly divisions of the year, should coordinate the various time units, and should arrange the weekday sequence so that weekdays and month-dates will agree and be identical in succeeding years—thus restoring the "perpetual" quality lost with the introduction of the seven-day week in A.D. 321.

The chief difficulty with the calendar is that there are 52 1/7 weeks in a 365-day year: the extra 1/7 of a week causes the weekday wanderings. And this is a serious defect in a system of measurement that should be as precise and invariable as our other scientific systems of measuring. The wanderings of the calendar are increasingly burdensome to an advancing civilization that demands accuracy, reliability and efficiency in its activities, its planning, its records and its statistics.

Inasmuch as the revised calendar is on the threshold of acceptance, there are doubtless many people who will welcome a brief account of the history of the movement and its background in the ancient and modern worlds.

The onward march of calendar reform to its goal is, I am convinced, inevitable. The proposed changes can be put into effect without serious dislocation or disturbance, and with many benefits that will prove of practical advantage and profit to everybody, everywhere.

The enactment of a revised calendar provides an immediate pattern of international cooperation, a tangible proof of world unity in action. This was emphasized in the Memorandum submitted to the United Nations by India, which stated in one of its final paragraphs: "The 365th day of the year in The World Calendar is proposed to be an international holiday, without any weekday name, dedicated simultaneously in every country of the world to the universal harmony and unity of mankind, thus knitting all races, creeds, peoples and nations into a closer bond of fellowship, creating world-wide citizenship in the 'One World.' The potentialities of 'Worldsday' for strengthening and promoting international peace among all nations are of great value."

When I undertook the leadership of the international movement for calendar reform in 1930, my first task was to confer with outstanding people, both at home and abroad, in an effort to organize and unite the widely scattered supporters of the cause. One of my earliest and most enlightening talks was with Mahatma Gandhi, whom I met in London.

For a whole evening I sat with him on the hearth of an old-fashioned coal-burning fireplace in his Knightsbridge residence and discussed the future of calendar revision. We found ourselves in complete agreement on the desirability of a change. This was what could be expected from the great leader. But he opened my eyes to the special situation in India, where there are about thirty different calendars in current use. "This results in unbelievable confusion," Gandhi said earnestly. "It would be a splendid thing if our 350,000,000 people could have a single national unified calendar. I am in favor of such a calendar. I am in favor of a standardized calendar for the whole world, just as I am in favor of a uniform coinage for all countries and a supplementary artificial language (like Esperanto) for all peoples."

After our interview, Gandhi issued a statement to the press, in which he said: "I have been informed of, and I welcome, the international movement for calendar reform. I am always ready to endorse any honest movement which will help to unify the peoples of the world."

Gandhi's belief in the need for an improved calendar encouraged many of India's leading statesmen and scholars to take up the matter. Among them was his friend and successor, Prime Minister Jawaharlal Nehru. Another enthusiast is an eminent scientist, Professor Meghnad N. Saha, head of the Institute of Nuclear Physics in Calcutta, who eventually became chairman of an official India committee on calendar matters. The report to this committee was the energizing force which led to India's reassuring action at the United Nations in 1953.

III
TIME—IMAGE OF ETERNITY

*Time was created as
an image of eternity.*
—Plato

WHAT IS A CALENDAR? According to my definition it is man's chart for reckoning days, planning affairs and dating events. It is a system of arranging the division and recording of Time into years, seasons, months, weeks and days best adapted to meet the purposes and activities of life.

Among these various time units, man learned after many centuries of trial and error that the *seasons* are at the very heart of the calendar. Their annual recurrence is the foundation upon which an effective and orderly measuring system must be built. From one winter to the next, or from one spring to the next, makes a year of approximately 365¼ days.

The seasons in their familiar and changeable aspects are the essential elements of Time. They are the givers of life and its bounty in their recurring periods of seeding, flowering, harvesting and dormancy. I am always impressed by their importance in the Biblical account of the Creation, "Let there be lights in the firmament of the heaven to divide the day from the night; and let them be for signs, and for seasons, and for days, and years."

The order—seasons, days, years—seems to me significant. Seasons are recognized as the foundation of Time. The annual recurrence of the seasons, the intermediary days, and the year as a complete and finished time unit constitute the calendar. With this principle established it is a dependable Time-measurer. Here is the blueprint for man to follow if he is to have a reliable standard time plan for his daily living and his daily activities.

Historians and philosophers tell us that some of the difficulties of constructing a calendar are due to the fact that it deals with an intangible element called Time. When we ask "What is Time?" we find ourselves facing a problem of the first magnitude. The dictionary gives numerous definitions, many of them baffling to the average mind. (1) Time is that order of phenomena in general by reference to which all permanence and change are predicated, usually conceived as a dimension of reality, distinguished from the spatial by the fact that the order of temporal succession is irreversible. (2) Time is the uninterrupted succession of days, years or events; the passing of the hours. (3) In philosophy, the oldest concept of Time is that of an absolute flowing, which is a reality apart from the events which fill it and which has a fixed uniform rate in terms of which all change is measured.

A British scientist, Clifford Troke, is easier to understand: "Time is a flow, differing from all other flows in this, that everything flows with it; since Time moves continually, all the devices which measure it involve motion—what we do is to take a certain regular motion, a movement as regular as possible, and keep it as a standard measure."

The scholarly poet, Henry W. Longfellow, one of my early favorites, makes a similar observation: "What is time?" he asks, and answers "The shadow on the dial, the striking of the clock, the running of the sand, day and night, summer and winter, months, years, centuries—these are but arbitrary and outward signs, the measure of Time, not Time itself. Time is the Life of the soul."

To us calendar reformers, Time is a universal force, constantly moving and governing man's life and all its activities. It is as much a part of man as his shadow. It is ever with us, yet ever elusive. We know it exists, but we can never actually define it nor possess it. Its influence is completely impersonal, universal and self-contained—qualities which must be inherent in any effective system of time measurement, whether, as we earlier pointed out, it be the clock or the calendar.

Throughout the ages the development of clocks and calendars has been singularly different. Clockmakers seem to have understood the scientific nature of Time; in dividing it into hours, minutes and seconds they carefully avoided extraneous influence. Not since the days of the ancient Babylonians have the hours been given religious, astrological or astronomical names or interpretations. The clock is strictly a scientific instrument by which the seconds, minutes and hours are counted. The result is that our clocks today are admirable in their accuracy, simplicity and universality. The same clock is observed throughout the world.

Contrast this simplicity and perfection with the

clumsy irregularities of the calendar, the result of tampering by alien hands and the injection of foreign and irrelevant ideas. Because of some peculiar human kink, the calendar has all too often been the target of people who used it for personal, religious or nationalistic purposes, or who took a possessive attitude toward it, thereby ignoring the broad universal and scientific requirements essential in time measurements.

The calendar is basically a scientific system of measuring Time—seasons, days and years—and whenever this basic foundation is interfered with the calendar becomes distorted and its rhythmic, balanced and harmonious flow is lost.

Here is the underlying error that has beset all efforts at calendar improvement, whether in ancient days or in our current century. By re-establishing the calendar on a purely scientific basis suitable to our civil and everyday life and arranging it in an orderly arithmetical pattern, we can make it as useful, reliable and efficient an instrument of Time as are our clocks and watches. Let us remember Alexander Pope's significant words: "Order is Heaven's first law."

IV

BY THE LIGHT OF
THE MOON

Thinketh, He dwelleth i' the cold o' the moon,
Thinketh He made it, with the sun to match.
—Robert Browning

WE HAVE SEEN that primitive man felt an urgent need of measuring Time and counting days. How he first met this need we do not know, but when history begins we find him using, in most cases, some kind of lunar calendar. As H. G. Wells wrote in his *Outline of History*, "The earliest recorded reckoning is by moons."

Primitive man was acutely conscious of the daily recurring light of day and dark of night. His normal pattern of life was to be active in the daytime and to sleep at night. He hunted, fished and foraged for food: he knew a little elementary agriculture and animal husbandry. He was chiefly concerned with his personal and tribal welfare—obtaining sufficient nourishment, clothing, shelter and protection from danger. Gradually on the road of civilization he began to use tallies; he counted the days on fingers and toes; he used sticks and stones for markers.

He was familiar with the nightly miracle of the moon,

which dominated the heavens during the hours of darkness. He was aware of its regular waxing and waning. He marvelled at the new moon's delicate crescent and the full moon's solid orb of light, which he hailed with rejoicing and feasting. He regarded the moon as more essential than the sun, "because it supplied light at night, when light was needed."

The moon was man's faithful friend and guide. Its recurring phases were regular and reliable—new moon, first half moon, full moon, second half moon. Here was a celestial chronometer, a heavenly calendar ready-made, providing unfailing markers from which he could count his days. The word *moon,* in its origin, means "measurer."

There are those who believe that the moon's phases, each of about seven days' duration, set apart the grouping of days which we know as a week. Likewise, the complete circuit of the moon's four phases became a moon-th or month.

Unfortunately the duration of a moon-month is not exactly four weeks of seven days each. It is about 29½ days. To meet this difficulty, primitive man added to his 28-day month an additional one or two days, the brief period of darkness when the moon was not visible in the sky, "when it had gone to sleep." His moon-months were figured at alternately 29 and 30 days.

Eventually the moon-th periods were put together in a bundle of twelve to complete a longer unit, a year. Twelve was a convenient number, easily divisible in all kinds of ways.

This lunar year of twelve moon-months, however, was shorter than the sun-year, which was vaguely marked off by the annual recurrences of the seasons and other climatic conditions. The seasonal year was one of the most important factors in life and could not be ignored. Yet twelve lunar months of alternating 29 and 30 days made up a year of only 354 days, while the sun-year required $365\frac{1}{4}$ days. The only way a lunar calendar could be adjusted to a fairly accurate seasonal year was to add a 13th month every two or three years, and this is what eventually happened to most lunar calendars.

In ancient days the priesthood was the guardian of the calendar, under whose direction the insertion of the 13th month was made. The priests were the scientists, the learned men, and the civil servants in the social and tribal life of primitive people.

Historically, lunar calendars belong to the infancy of the human race. The moon's phases were something that could be easily observed, that required no printed tables, no great effort and little imagination.

Moon calendars were reasonably adequate at this early stage of man's development when his outlook on life was restricted to his tribe and his immediate environment. The moon was the satellite that belonged to the planet earth. Primitive man had not as yet progressed to the greater knowledge that the earth belonged to a vast solar system of which the sun was the central and motivating force. The lesser light of the moon had a limiting and also an emotional effect upon early man which encouraged magic, sorcery, superstition and taboo.

As civilization advanced and developed, the inadequacies of moon reckoning grew more and more apparent. The insertion of an occasional extra month to obtain agreement with the seasonal year became in-

creasingly urgent and the method amazingly complicated. It was in the march of progress that non-seasonal
moon calendars should give way to the sun calendar,
which automatically recognized the indispensable seasons. It became increasingly evident that a sun calendar
had to be separated completely from the moon if it was
to be simple, useful and adequate. To serve two masters
simultaneously is always difficult.

MOON-MONTH CALENDAR

First month	30 days	Seventh month	30 days
Second month	29 days	Eighth month	29 days
Third month	30 days	Ninth month	30 days
Fourth month	29 days	Tenth month	29 days
Fifth month	30 days	Eleventh month	30 days
Sixth month	29 days	Twelfth month	29 or 30 days

Occasional Thirteenth month

(Twelve lunations equal 354.37 days)

V

WHERE FLOWS THE NILE

It flows through old hushed Egypt and its sands,
Like some grave mighty thought threading a dream.
—Leigh Hunt

HISTORY'S OLDEST fixed date, 4236 B.C., marks an epoch-making devolopment in the calendar. This was the year when Egypt accepted the sun as the central influence in Time measurement. Its astronomers and wise men had developed a remarkably accurate solar calendar, the adoption of which is the first recorded event in the annals of the human race. By a bold enactment the calendar became completely separated from all lunar reckonings; moon-months were abandoned and the month became an independent time unit, a convenient subdivision of a twelve-month solar year.

Professor Henry W. Breasted, the eminent American Egyptologist, was the first to call attention to the significance of this event, which he described as "the earliest date in the intellectual history of mankind." The Swedish historian Martin P. Nilsson had already assembled impressive documentation to show that "the Egyptian calendar is the greatest intellectual fact in the history of time reckoning." The underlying motives of this development, he indicated, were practical convenience and utility, as well as astronomical accuracy.

The early Egyptians were a superior people, masters of mathematics and practical science. They carved out a time pattern which (with few modifications) is still in use today, almost 6,200 years later. Its originators were undaunted pioneers in the recording of Time, far in advance of other nations. For many centuries, the Egyptians enjoyed the greatest civilization of their day. Living under clear cloudless skies that were bright with sunlight by day and brilliant with starlight at night, their astronomers made close and constant observations of the movements of the sun and other heavenly bodies. The pyramids, erected as monuments to illustrious rulers, were astronomical observatories by means of which they could study the skies, observe the shadows cast upon the earth, and make painstaking records of heavenly phenomena which enabled them to analyze and foretell climatic and seasonal changes.

It was highly necessary for the Egyptians to know in advance the date of the annual overflowing of the life-giving River Nile, upon which depended the fertility of their soil. Their people, then as now, were predominantly agricultural. The area of tillable soil was so restricted and the density of the population so great that any failure to take full advantage of the inundation meant famine and distress.

The astronomers discovered that the annual Nile flood appeared simultaneously with the yearly appearance on the morning horizon of Egypt's brightest star, Sirius or Sothis—the Dog Star. This occurred on the date which we know as July 19. The coincidence of the "three risings"—sunrise, the rising of Sirius and the rising of the Great River—was an event of supreme importance to all Egyptians. The astronomers made it the basis of the calendar, for by a simple mathematical counting of days from the previous heliacal rising of Sirius, they could predict with sufficient accuracy the inundation of the Nile, and the whole nation could be prepared for it.

Their solar calendar had twelve months each of 30 days, making a year of 360 days. The months, mystically identified with the twelve constellations of the zodiac along the celestial ecliptic, were each subdivided into three "decads" of ten days. The arrangement of 36 decads within a year of twelve 30-day months is considered the source of the 360-degree circle and its subdivisions, still used for measuring angles by mathematicians, surveyors and navigators.

The Egyptian astronomers were of course aware that a 360-day year was too short and did not fully agree with the seasons. They corrected this discrepancy by adding five "extra" days at the end of every year as special feast days. This gave the year a total of 365 days, which was fairly accurate. Thus the Egyptians were not only the first people to adopt a solar calendar that recognized the seasons, but also the first to acknowledge the year as a complete and integrated unit of Time, within which the intermediary time units fitted perfectly.

Thomas Mann in his trilogy on Joseph tells how this young Israelite was brought to Egypt and became fascinated with the "mystery of numbers" and the "divineness residing in measure." He learned that the stations of the zodiac were twelve in number, that the "moon number" was seven. He pondered on the mystery of the solar calendar of 360 days, supplemented by the annually inserted five-day period which brought the year to the necessary 365 days. He marvelled at the order, harmony and satisfaction of the calendar.

Egypt flourished under the stimulus of its newly organized civil time system. A primitive country with an unreliable economy became powerful and prosperous. Famines were less frequent. The way of life became simpler, easier and more orderly. Professor Breasted tells us that the adoption of the solar calendar "was thus the beginning of a great movement in human life which carried over the thought of man from the world of nature to the world of human life." It was an epochal step in the social and civil development of man that called for an audacious act of vision and conviction—but honest conviction always calls for audacity and courage.

Comparing the Egyptians with other nations of the same period, it has been observed that "when they discarded the lunar calendar and accepted the solar standard they gained a broader outlook and the beginning of a world awareness."

This was strikingly apparent about 1365 B.C. when there appeared a remarkable ruler named Akhenaton (Ikhnaton). Under his dynamic rule, man began to feel a thrill of universalism. He was "the first prophet of internationalism," the first Egyptian to believe in a universal God for all mankind—the shining sun-god, the light of the world, to whom all creatures and races of man belonged. His great hymn to Aton, the Sun, has come down to us in the 104th Psalm:

O Lord, thou art very great,
Thou art clothed with honor and majesty
And robed with light as with a garment
Thou hast stretched out the heavens like a tent
And made the clouds thy chariot,
The winds thy messengers, fire and flame thy ministers.
Thou dost cause the grass to grow for the cattle
And plants for the service of man,
That he may bring forth food from the earth.
Thou hast made the moon to mark the seasons
And the sun knoweth its going down.
Thou makest darkness and it is night;
The sun rises: man goes forth to his work
And to his labor until the evening.
O Lord, how manifold are thy works!
In wisdom hast thou made them all:
The earth is full of thy creatures,
They all look to thee to give them their food in due season;
When thou givest to them, they gather it up,
When thou openest thy hand, they are filled with good
    things,
When thou hidest thy face, they are dismayed,
When thou sendest forth thy spirit, they are created,
And thou renewest the face of the earth.

Three thousand years after the adoption of the Egyptian time system, Akhenaton's emphasis on the spiritual significance of the sun gave new meaning to the solar calendar and the vital part it exerted in the development, prosperity and world leadership of his country.

Yet the astronomers had come to know that the Egyptian calendar was not perfect. They had learned that the solar year was actually a quarter of a day longer than 365 days. Because of this discrepancy the time-star Sirius arose a day late every four years, so that eventually the Egyptian calendar revolved entirely around the solar year. Of course the priestly astronomers allowed for this error in their calculations of the seasons and in their predictions of the Nile floods. But it was an awkward arrangement.

To remove this incongruity, Ptolemy III in 238 B.C. decided to set the calendar right with the seasons. His proposal was to insert an additional day every four years to the group of the five year-end feast days. He ordered the change in an edict preserved on the famous Canopus Stone (discovered in 1886), in which he quaintly dedicated the extra day every four years to the "Good Doing Gods."

Notwithstanding Ptolemy's staunch support, the plan was defeated. Old custom was too firmly entrenched. The influential priest-astronomers opposed it as an encroachment on their prerogatives and the public through apathy and indifference let them have their way. Thus progress was thwarted and an illogical and unscientific pattern was perpetuated.

Two centuries later, Ptolemy's rejected proposition was enthusiastically adopted by the Roman ruler Julius Caesar, and the extra day became the quadrennial leap-year day in a more accurate solar calendar that immediately went into international operation throughout the far-flung dominions of the Roman Empire.

EGYPTIAN CALENDAR:
(Twelve Months: Every month the same)

First Decade:	1	2	3	4	5	6	7	8	9	10
Second Decade:	11	12	13	14	15	16	17	18	19	20
Third Decade:	21	22	23	24	25	26	27	28	29	30

(Five additional days added at the end of every year)

VI

RENDER UNTO CAESAR

Methods of measuring time grew up about the need for determining the dates of the tabooed or holy days, and for fixing and recording the occurrence of unusual natural phenomena which were believed to have some regular significance. . . . The perfection of the methods of measuring time has been a gradual transition "from luck to mathematics."

—Harry Elmer Barnes

OF ALL BIZARRE and primitive calendars, that of the early Romans reached the height of absurdity and confusion. It was an old tribal system, inherited by the legendary first ruler Romulus when he founded Rome in 753 B.C., later recorded as 1 A.U.C. (anno urbis conditae). This calendar consisted of ten lunar months, beginning with the spring moon in March and ending about 300 days later in December. The period between December and March was disregarded, being an interval of little importance because "nothing happened" during those slumbering cold dark 60 days.

In keeping with an ancient custom the origin of which had long been lost, the months were divided into three sections known as Kalends, Nones and Ides, each of different length. The word Kalends, meaning a "calling" or announcement of a new month, gave us the word *calendar*.

Romulus lived 34 centuries after the Egyptians originated and founded their remarkable solar calendar. It is one of the ironies of history that the early Romans had no knowledge of this achievement, which eventually they had to blend into their own system, but only after many centuries of struggle with their primitive tribal heritage.

The ten-month calendar was hopeless, having none of the elements of stability and regularity that a satisfactory system of time measurement requires. Romulus did nothing about it, probably because he was without knowledge of mathematics and astronomy. His successor, Numa Pompilius, was more intelligent and scholarly, fully recognizing that the calendar needed improvement. In his long reign of 53 years he had ample time to become a constructive calendar reformer.

He increased the number of months from ten to twelve by adding January and February. The months were still lunar in character, their lengths alternating between 29 and 30 days. This gave the year 354 days but as the total was an even number and to the Romans this was unlucky, an extra 355th day was added at the end of the year.

Numa was advised by his astronomers that the extra 355th day would not be sufficient to agree with the seasons—which were important not only in agriculture but in military operations as well. To overcome this defect, Numa did what other calendar makers have done; he inserted an additional thirteenth month every two years, calling it Mercedonius (from the Latin word for wages, indicating that it meant extra remuneration). This "remunerative" month of 22 or 23 days was arbitrarily thrust into the calendar toward the end of February, after the 23rd, when the newly inserted month began. When it was finished, the remaining five or six days of February carried on. Of all the complicated man-made calendar adjustments in history, this was certainly the most fantastic.

Realizing that the awkward thirteenth month needed some authoritative supervision, Numa assigned it to the Pontifex Maximus, head of his newly created College of Pontiffs. He failed to realize that this would lead to all kinds of abuse—that the occasional 13th month would become a "political plum" which clever and unscrupulous officials could manipulate for their own purpose. By lengthening or shortening the intervals between intercalations, friends could be kept in power, enemies removed, dates advanced or postponed and all kinds of schemes promoted. And that is just what happened. Through the years such tampering with the calendar caused it to fall into chaos. The original intent to keep the calendar in line with the seasons was lost, so that in the first century B.C. the spring equinox had strayed from its place by about three months.

Meanwhile there had been other efforts which violated the calendar. About 300 B.C. a lawyer-politician named Cneius Flavius persuaded the people that all the months should have an odd number of days in order to make them lucky. February was the only exception; being the last month of the year it was unlucky, so it was shortened to 28 days. The result:

March	31 days	7th month	(September)	29 days
April	29 days	8th month	(October)	31 days
May	31 days	9th month	(November)	29 days
June	29 days	10th month	(December)	29 days
Quintilis	31 days	11th month	(January)	29 days
Sextilis	29 days	12th month	(February)	28 days

355 days

The intercalary month Mercedonius—22 or 23 days— was inserted every two years before the last five days in February to adjust the lunar year to the seasons. A Flavian cycle of four years had 355, 378, 355 and 377 days, giving an average of 366¼ days, or one day in excess of the seasonal year. If this had been meticulously followed from the time of Flavius to the time of Caesar, the Roman calendar would have been about 250 days out of step with the seasons, but actually the observance of the Flavian rules was irregular and indefinite, and historians have difficulty in assigning correct dates to historical events in those years.

Another political interference with the calendar came in 153 B.C. when the beginning of the year was changed from the spring equinoctial date, March 25, to January 1. The new date had no scientific or seasonal significance, but was the appointed time for newly elected consuls to assume their civic duties. The populace considered this event as appropriate for the beginning of a new year so that, first by custom and later by official enactment, January 1 became the new year—a political date.

One of the incongruous results (which is still with us) was that the month named Quintilis, or "fifth," actually became the seventh month: and so with all the other numbered months—Sextilis, September, October, November and December. Romans were so keenly conscious of this absurdity that it became a pastime of the emperors to re-name the six numbered months according to their individual whims. September was known at various times as Germanicus, Antoninus and Tacitus; November was Domitianus, Faustinus and Romanus. Fortunately none of these names lasted very long.

Julius Caesar was the great reformer who made the Roman calendar the standard of the Western world. He had experienced the irregularities and difficulties of the Roman system while he was a military commander in Gaul, so that when he arrived in Rome, calendar revision was one of his chief concerns. While in Egypt, he had learned about that country's superior solar calendar, which caused him to appoint the Greek astronomer, Sosigenes of Alexandria, to be his chief adviser in revising the Roman system.

Caesar's authority to deal with this matter came through his election to the post of Pontifex Maximus in 63 B.C. After extensive studies, he put his new reform into effect in 45 B.C. The preceding year was one of the biennial periods which included the inserted month of Mercedonius. It became known as the "Year of Confusion." Caesar took the 355-day year with its inserted Mercedonius of 23 days and then added two more months making it 445 days long, a drastic operation which brought the calendar into step with the seasons. (The two added months were Undecember, 33 days, and Duodecember, 34 days.)

Caesar was wise in accepting without hesitation the Egyptian solar year of 12 months, with two changes. He distributed the last five days of the year (a festival period in Egypt) more evenly throughout the calendar, and he adopted Ptolemy's previously rejected extra leap-year day ("Good Doing Gods") by adding it to February every four years. The calendar was fixed at 365 days in ordinary years and 366 days in leap years. In recognition of this outstanding reform a grateful Senate honored Julius Caesar by re-naming his birth-month Quintilis, July.

As compared with the Egyptian system, Caesar's adaptation was a considerable improvement. The reduction of the intercalary period from five days every year to one day every four years lifted the Roman calendar to a new level of efficiency and convenience. It was obvious to the scholarly Sosigenes that the shorter the period of intercalation, the better the calendar.

The new leap-year day was inserted after the 23rd of February, where the 13th month of Mercedonius had been previously intercalated. Thus the 24th of February —in Roman terminology "the 6th day before the Kalends of March"—was repeated in leap years and became a double-six or bissextilis. This is the origin of the term bissextile given by Europeans to the leap-year day. Speaking historically, the added day in our present leap years is actually the old "double" 24th of February—which makes the month 29 days long instead of 28.

Two Latin historians, Censorinus and Macrobius, explain the operation thus: To the old calendar of 355 days Caesar added ten days in order to make it a solar calendar. To January, March, May, Quintilis (July), Sextilis (August), October and December he gave each 31 days; and to April, June, September and November each 30 days. But February, the unlucky month of Terminalia, was left unchanged, "so that the religious rites of the gods of the nether world might not be disturbed." In this manner Caesar gave to seven months 31 days (the lucky odd number) and to four months 30 days (the unlucky even number).

The arrangement of the 31-day and 30-day months was not as regular and simple as it might have been, but presumably this did not particularly concern Caesar. We are historically quite certain that the arrangement of the months was as we have it today.

A different version of his calendar plan was published in the 1830 edition of the *Encyclopedia Britannica,* and gained wide currency before it was disproved many years later by the evidence of newly discovered inscriptions. This theoretical reconstruction of Roman history suggested that Julius Caesar set up an improved arrangement of the months, with alternating months of 31 days and 30 days, and that his arrangement was altered by his successor, Augustus, in order to give August as many days as July. The reason for the change, said *Britannica,* was Augustan vanity.

But such a foolish gesture of vanity is out of character in one of Rome's greatest and most far-sighted emperors, and the accusation against him was disproved when Italian archeologists uncovered monuments with inscriptions clearly showing that Sextilis had 31 days before it was re-named August.

Caesar did not pretend to have given the world a perfect calendar. All he claimed was that his plan was a great improvement on what had gone before. He established a solar calendar that recognized the seasons within a fixed and complete year, a worthy successor to the more ancient Egyptian solar calendar.

He did not disturb the awkward division of the months into Ides, Nones and Kalends, from which comes the old Latin-class mnemonic:

> In March, July, October, May,
> The Ides are on the fifteenth day,
> The Nones the seventh; all other months besides
> Have two days less for Nones and Ides.

He must have been keenly aware of the superiority of the Egyptian arrangement of subdividing the months into three groups of ten days each. Nor did he change the beginning of the year to a seasonal point, the spring equinox or the winter solstice.

He had this latter improvement clearly in mind, but he was deterred from carrying it out because in 45 B.C. the first of January occurred on the new moon—and it was the new moon, still in high favor with a superstitious populace, that made him compromise and leave the New Year alone. Many astronomers and historians have pointed out certain advantages that would have resulted had Caesar placed the beginning of the calendar year on a really scientific basis.

Perhaps Caesar would have carried his reform further had he lived longer. He was assassinated on the Ides of March, a few months after the new calendar came into use.

During the years that followed, the unfamiliar leap-year rule was misinterpreted by the College of Pontiffs. Instead of inserting an extra day every four years, they observed leap year every three years. This caused the calendar once again to shift from its seasonal moorings, and it was Caesar's nephew, the Emperor Augustus, who undertook to correct the error. He cancelled all leap years between 8 B.C. and A.D. 8, and directed that thereafter all leap years should fall as originally intended. Once again the Roman Senate gave honor to a calendar reformer by re-naming Sextilis, August, which the Emperor considered his auspicious month.

This pattern was in continuous use until it was re-adjusted in 1582 by Pope Gregory XIII.

CALENDAR AFTER JULIUS CAESAR
(Solar Year of 365¼ days)

January	31 days	July	31 days
February	28 or 29 days	August	31 days
March	31 days	September	30 days
April	30 days	October	31 days
May	31 days	November	30 days
June	30 days	December	31 days

365 or 366 days

VII

CONSTANTINE AND THE WEEK

Upon the first day of the week, the disciples came together to break bread.

—Acts 20:7

CONSTANTINE, the Roman Emperor who has been called "a great historical phenomenon," was a constructive statesman of boundless energy and daring, who saved a tottering empire. He came to the throne from distant Britain, where his father had set up a capital at York to govern the tributary provinces of Western Europe, including the areas which are now France, Spain, Germany, Scandinavia and the Low Countries.

His interest in the calendar stemmed from his tolerant attitude toward the Christians, who were a valuable part of his military and civil personnel. In Rome, the Diocletian persecutions of the Christians had reached a climax of inhuman cruelty, but Constantine was never a participant. Boldly taking the opposite side, he marched into his decisive battle against Rome with the cross of Christ on his banners and an inspired motto that "through this sign thou shalt conquer."

As Emperor, he did not make Christianity the sole religion of the state. To the end of his days, he bore the title Pontifex Maximus as chief priest of the ancient pagan Roman hierarchy. But at the same time he gave Christianity complete equality with the traditional official worship. The coins which he issued carry both the cross and the images of Mars and Jupiter. Personally, he leaned more and more toward the Christians and on his death bed became one of them.

He had always been impressed with the Christian ideas about the calendar. He liked their observance of a seven-day week, with the *first day* set aside as a day of rest and worship. The week was a complete novelty to the Roman calendar, which had its months subdivided into the impractical Nones, Ides and Kalends.

Nine years after Constantine became Emperor he issued an edict introducing the seven-day week into the Julian calendar. The weekdays had no names but were known only by numbers. The week displaced the old Kalends, Nones and Ides, and eventually the days acquired the names of the seven heavenly bodies—Sun, Moon, Mars, Mercury, Jupiter, Venus and Saturn.

Unfortunately, Constantine in introducing the week did not give the matter the full scientific consideration it deserved. He did not realize that he was removing from the Julian calendar the *perpetual* characteristic which had been one of its chief merits. Julius Caesar had established a calendar that was exactly the same year after year; even the bissextile observance in leap year did not disturb the perpetuity of the calendar. But now, with the new seven-day week gradually gaining outstanding importance in time measurement, the Roman calendar lost this desirable perpetual feature. The weekdays rotated, and every year became different from the preceding and following one.

The change must have been annoying to the Romans and all their satellites, from Britain to India, because the monumental permanent calendars which had been erected in every part of the empire—carved in stone—had now become useless. In adopting the week, the imperial authorities had not given any consideration to the fact that 52 1/7 weeks within a 365-day year would involve difficult adjustments and recurring confusions. They carelessly thought of the year as 52 weeks; but the period of 52 weeks was always short a day to complete a true solar year—so at the end of each year a day must be borrowed from the first week of the next year. The New Year could never begin consecutively on the first day of the week. The perpetual calendar was lost.

Had Constantine foreseen the effect of his action, he probably would have made adjustments. The device of intercalation was familiar in many regional calendars of his contemporary world: for example, in Egypt, Greece and Palestine. He might easily have hit upon the idea of a supplementary day without a weekday name, and thus he could have preserved the entity of the year which had been so carefully maintained in the Egyptian and Julian systems.

Thus the wandering week became the chief difficulty with the calendar, a serious defect that has continued ever since, and one that will be remedied at long last with the adoption of The World Calendar.

The origin of the week is historically a question that goes back further than any existing record. It was introduced into Palestine from the Assyrians, who used the seven weekdays as symbols for the seven heavenly bodies which were the basis of their astrology. The astrological belief was that each hour of the day was governed by a different "planet," in the order of their supposed distance from the Earth—Saturn, Jupiter, Mars, Sun, Venus, Mercury and Moon. The "planet" which governed the first hour of the day was called its *Regent*. If the Sun was regent for the first day, then the regents for the following days were: Moon, Mars, Mercury, Jupiter, Venus and Saturn—the same order of days that we observe in the week today. (In the Teutonic languages we have replaced the midweek deities with their counterparts— Tiu, Woden, Thor and Freya.)

But further back than the Assyrians, it is probable that the seven-day week was related in the earlier lunar calendars to the four phases of the moon, each about seven days in duration. Actually there were several kinds of "weeks" used. The early Romans observed an eight-day market week; other tribal and primitive people had market weeks of four, five or six days; the Egyptians and Greeks divided their months into ten-day periods.

Whatever its origin, the week with its one day of spiritual observance has proved a time unit of profound significance and high value to the human race. Through Constantine's decree the week received its *right beginning,* Sunday, observed by the Christians in commemoration of the Resurrection, and its *right ending,* Saturday, honored by the Jews and Seventh-Day Adventists as the sacred day of rest. A deep significance has ever been attached to beginning and ending the week on the highest spiritual note. Friday remains the religious day of the Moslems, the Hegira, when Mohammed was forced to flee from Mecca. Even those for whom the week has no religious connotation would not think of abandoning the seven-day week, an interval of Time that fits perfectly into the spiritual and practical living of peoples everywhere. The inherent benefits of one day of rest and worship are universally recognized. Mankind and the calendar are enriched and ennobled with its observance.

CONSTANTINE'S INTRODUCTION OF THE WEEK in A.D. 321 changed the stable Roman Calendar into a variable system, in which every year was different:

January 321

S	M	T	W	T	F	S
1	2	3	4	5	6	7
8	9	10	11	12	13	14
15	16	17	18	19	20	21
22	23	24	25	26	27	28
29	30	31				

January 322

S	M	T	W	T	F	S
	1	2	3	4	5	6
7	8	9	10	11	12	13
14	15	16	17	18	19	20
21	22	23	24	25	26	27
28	29	30	31			

January 323

S	M	T	W	T	F	S
		1	2	3	4	5
6	7	8	9	10	11	12
13	14	15	16	17	18	19
20	21	22	23	24	25	26
27	28	29	30	31		

January 324

S	M	T	W	T	F	S
			1	2	3	4
5	6	7	8	9	10	11
12	13	14	15	16	17	18
19	20	21	22	23	24	25
26	27	28	29	30	31	

January 325

S	M	T	W	T	F	S
					1	2
3	4	5	6	7	8	9
10	11	12	13	14	15	16
17	18	19	20	21	22	23
24	25	26	27	28	29	30
31						

January 326

S	M	T	W	T	F	S
						1
2	3	4	5	6	7	8
9	10	11	12	13	14	15
16	17	18	19	20	21	22
23	24	25	26	27	28	29
30	31					

These presentations of the calendar in Constantine's time are merely theoretical. The division of the months by Ides, Nones and Kalends was dropped during the Middle Ages.

VIII

GREGORY'S CONTRIBUTION

The time is out of joint; O cursed spite,
That ever I was born to set it right!
—Shakespeare

AFTER CONSTANTINE, 1,250 years passed before another change in the calendar occurred. In 1582 Pope Gregory XIII undertook the revision now in general use.

In the intervening medieval centuries (between the fifth and sixteenth) a number of important events had a lasting impact upon Western civilization. The reign of Charlemagne in the eighth and ninth centuries brought together in a new unity many of the Northern peoples of Europe. The Arabic contributions to the West in the fields of science, mathematics, art and education reached their peak in the tenth century. The Norman invasion in the eleventh century forced the islanders of Great Britain into the European arena. The eight Crusades between the eleventh and thirteenth centuries gave Europe a closer contact with the Near East. The Magna Carta of the thirteenth century freed Englishmen from feudal lords and barons. The Gutenberg printing press of the fifteen century led to a broader dissemination of learning. The discovery of America in the fifteenth century stimulated almost every phase of human activity in the Old World. The Reformation of the sixteenth century lifted men's conscience from the domination of state religions. Everywhere there were driving forces urging mankind forward toward new freedoms, broader knowledge and greater unity.

The calendar of Caesar and Constantine, with its irregularities and deficiencies, could not escape these forces. As early as the thirteenth century scholars and public officials complained that the calendar year was drifting away from the seasons, because under Caesar's four-year rule too many leap years had been inserted. The resultant difficulties were repeatedly called to the attention of rulers and popes, but nothing was done until the latter years of Gregory's occupancy of the pontifical throne.

The aging Pope, weary of wars and public works and financial difficulties, turned his attention at last to the calendar. Aided by a notable staff of scientists, he analyzed the problems. *First,* how could the year be brought back into accord with the seasons? *Second,* how could the leap-year rule be corrected to stop further dislocation? *Third,* could the beginning of the year be set in a fixed position, instead of being observed at different times by different peoples? *Fourth,* could anything be done about the wandering Easter, a cause of considerable inconvenience?

The Easter question was actually the source of the Papal intervention. Easter was a spring festival, but the "drifting" of the calendar had been gradually pushing it further and further away from the spring equinox. Eventually, if not corrected, Easter would be arriving in the winter, and this would correspondingly dislocate all the other important feasts which depended on it. Julius Caesar had kept the equinox on the ancient date of March 25; in Gregory's time it was falling on the 11th.

The error in Caesar's leap-year rule was readily understood. The Roman Emperor had figured the solar year at 365¼ days. Actually it takes the earth but 365 days, 5 hours, 48 minutes and 46 seconds to complete its annual journey around the sun. The true year is thus 11 minutes and 14 seconds short of six hours—a quarter of the 24-hour day. This slight difference, accumulating through the centuries, had been sufficient to put the calendar 14 days off balance with the seasons.

Pope Gregory and his scientists decided to deal with the first of their four calendar problems by dropping a certain number of days from the year 1582. On the question of "How many days?" they worked out a compromise. Not the full 14 which would have brought things back to Caesar's formula, but only ten days, which adjusted the equinoctial date to March 21, where it had been observed at the time of the first Christian conclave at Nicea in A.D. 325. The use of Nicea as a starting point gave an ecclesiastical touch to the whole operation.

As to Problem Number Two, the new leap-year rule, skillfully formulated by the Pope's advisers, related only to century years. Those which were divisible by 400 were to be leap years; all the others were to be ordinary years, such as 1700, 1800, 1900. The years 1600 and 2000 are leap years. Outside of centurial years, all the other years keep to the simple four-year rule as prescribed by Caesar. Thus three leap years are dropped out of each

400 years, and this simple formula will keep the calendar approximately correct with the seasons for about 3,300 years from the time of the Gregorian Reform.

Problem Number Three was concerned with a stable New Year's Day. For many centuries, the New Year had been the most wayward of anniversaries. Julius Caesar had accepted January 1, but in the sixth century the Church had adopted March 25, the Feast of the Annunciation, which mystically recalled the birth of Christ. During succeeding centuries, this was a widely observed date, although all kinds of variations occurred from time to time. Germany and Spain thought the year should begin at Christmas, Denmark used an August New Year's Day, France and the Netherlands observed Easter. In Venice the date was March 1, in Ireland February 1.

To remove all the confusion Pope Gregory came out firmly for January 1. He ignored the pagan origin of this date, and gave it ecclesiastical standing by pointing out that it was the Feast of Circumcision in the church calendar. His scientific advisers probably reminded him that the first of January had a certain astronomical basis: the "perihelion" occurs on or about the beginning of January, when the earth is closest to the sun—being 91,500,000 miles away, as against 95,000,000 miles six months later.

Then there was the question of stabilizing Easter. The wandering character of Easter is due to the fact that it is tied to a lunar reckoning; theoretically Easter comes on the first Sunday after the full moon following the spring equinox. Here is a basic contradiction. The civil calendar goes by the sun; the religious feast day Easter is reckoned by the moon. No compromise is possible, for the result must be either one thing or the other.

There appears to be no reason why Easter cannot be observed on the Sunday nearest to the historical date of the Resurrection, presumably April 9. Gregory and his advisers attempted no such change. They left Easter as it was, and the result is a wandering festival which causes great inconvenience in countries where Easter is important in civil life.

The Gregorian revision went into effect in 1582 in all Roman Catholic countries. Ten days were dropped from October: Thursday, October 4, was followed by Friday, October 15.

Outside the strictly Roman Catholic countries, there were long delays in recognizing the scientific advantages of Gregory's proposals. Protestant Germany and Denmark adopted the new calendar in 1700, Great Britain and the American colonies in 1752, Sweden in 1753, Japan in 1873, China in 1912. Russia and the Eastern Orthodox countries were tardiest of all—Russia first in 1918 and again in 1940 after experimenting with calendars of her own; and the Eastern Orthodox countries in 1924 and 1927.

The hesitancy of the Northern nations to accept the Gregorian reform was due to the violent religious prejudices aroused by the Reformation. In the Eastern Orthodox area, too, the scientific nature of the reform was minimized and the priesthood feared that acceptance would be interpreted as a quasi-allegiance to a faith different from their own.

In other parts of the world, particularly in the Asiatic countries, the new system was labelled the "Christian Calendar" and its name created resistance among Hindus, Moslems, Buddhists, Taoists and other powerful groups.

These unfortunate reactions had not been foreseen by Gregory XIII and his advisers, who had expected that the revision would be accepted as a sound scientific action without religious connotations. It did not work that way. For more than a century, his calendar was held up as a symbol of Papal domination, and this caused the Roman Catholic Church a considerable amount of annoyance and trouble. It is one of the reasons, in the present age, that the Vatican—although in favor of revision—has been reluctant to take any *initiative* in the movement for a further improvement in the calendar.

The Gregorian reform was good up to a point. It anchored the calendar in the seasonal year from which it never should have strayed, and it established a uniform practice as to the year's beginning. It failed, however, to correct Caesar's faulty arrangement of months, quarters and half years; and it did nothing to harmonize the wandering weekdays which were an inheritance from Constantine. These two faults are becoming increasingly burdensome with the development of civilization and the requirements of our modern world.

Gregory's able scientific advisers undoubtedly pointed out these defects. Such competent men as Lilius, Clavius and Scalliger could not have failed to realize the situation. The Pope's viewpoint, however, was strongly ecclesiastical: his primary concern was to make certain that the inconveniences of the church calendar were remedied, and he may have felt that any further action would endanger the simpler program he had in mind.

The Gregorian reform left the calendar still inadequate. There was no regularity in the arrangement of the months; the quarter years varied from 90 to 92 days in length; the half years were ridiculously unequal. The weekdays continued to wander from year to year, so that people actually had to use 14 different calendars and 28 different kinds of months. A new calendar had to be prepared and printed every year. The order, stability and comparability which only come when the year is one complete unit, such as the Egyptians and Julius Caesar recognized, were totally absent. The ideal of a perpetual and balanced measuring system of Time had to wait until the present twentieth century, when the pressures of science, business and a need for world unity would make imperative a further scientific simplification and perfection of the civil calendar.

It is a remarkable historic coincidence that at the very time when Gregory was wrestling with European calendar problems, the same sort of thing was happening in India. That then faraway country was enjoying the beneficent rule of Akber, greatest of the Mogul (Mongol) emperors and one of the most eminent royal personalities of all time. Much of his work of consolidation and organization in India survives to this day—and part of it involved an effort at unifying the Indian calendars.

Although Akber was unquestionably the greatest world figure of his century, he had to live within his limitations. One of these was that he knew practically nothing about the Western world except through a few contacts with Jesuit missionaries. His religion was a narrow form of Mohammedanism, which was a minority sect in India—even then a kaleidoscope of religions. In searching for an improved calendar, he never thought of consulting Europe and probably never heard of the Gregorian reform of 1582. Instead, he turned to Persia and its Jelali solar calendar, which he brought to India in 1584. It was one of the best of all solar calendars, with an even better approximation of the actual astronomical year than the Gregorian system.

Unfortunately Akber's reform measure was misunderstood, and after his death, in the absence of any central guidance, it became combined with ancient errors and local variations. Thus his main purpose of providing a national calendar was defeated. But it was a worthy attempt, and the broad vision which inspired it has always been recognized in India, and is indeed the foundation for the present movement under Nehru's leadership.

The world of today would be a better world had Akber and Pope Gregory joined forces in the 1580s. They would have emerged with a world-wide calendar, which would have drawn together the East and the West. The result would have been a powerful vehicle for international cooperation and understanding, qualities which remove narrow sectarianism and isolationist nationalism.

GREGORIAN CALENDAR
(Weekday arrangement varies each year)

January	31 days	July	31 days
February	28 or 29 days	August	31 days
March	31 days	September	30 days
First Quarter	90 or 91 days	Third Quarter	92 days
April	30 days	October	31 days
May	31 days	November	30 days
June	30 days	December	31 days
Second Quarter	91 days	Fourth Quarter	92 days

(First half year 181 or 182 days; second half year 184 days)

IX

CENTURY OF PREPARATION

New times demand new measures and new men;
The world advances, and in time outgrows
The laws that in our fathers' day were best.
— James Russell Lowell

MODERN CALENDAR REFORM was initiated in 1834 by an Italian priest, mathematician and philosopher, Abbé Marco Mastrofini. In that year he published a scholarly book with the impressive title *Amplissimi Frutti da Raccogliersi sul Calandario Gregoriano Perpetuo*—which may be freely translated "Final Results of Research on Perpetualizing the Gregorian Calendar." The volume was received by the Church with three *Nihil Obstats* and two *Imprimaturs*.

The Abbé proposed a year of 364 days—beginning with Sunday, January 1, and ending with a 365th "extra-calendrical" day, to be called *feria octava* (the holy day or the eighth weekday). In leap years there would be another extra day (to be placed either after February, as in the Gregorian calendar, or immediately after *feria octava*) which would be called "intercalary day." Mastrofini was thus the great pioneer for the stabilizing days which calendar reformers subsequently have adopted.

A recent Catholic writer points out: "The only detail in which he did not anticipate proposals like the modern World Calendar was in regularizing the length of the months and making the quarters equal. But these are, after all, lesser details. Mastrofini originated the basic idea of all modern reform, the stabilizing days. For this momentous suggestion he has not been adequately honored by the world."

Fifteen years after the publication of Mastrofini's book, the French philosopher Auguste Comte used the intercalary days in his 13-month "Positivist Calendar," as part of a vast scheme for human betterment, but no organized campaign for calendar reform developed until 1887 when the French astronomer Camille Flammarion, as president of the new Astronomical Society of France, initiated an ambitious contest for the most practical plan of calendar revision. The two prizes were won by slightly different 12-month proposals, both using Mastrofini's intercalary days.

The impact of the competition and the awards was world-wide. Flammarion had made an excellent beginning toward creating a universal interest, but his own preoccupations in the astronomical field prevented him from the necessary follow through.

The real impetus for an improved calendar did not come from either priests or astronomers, but from the world's leading business organization, the International Chamber of Commerce. This influential institution had been interested in calendar revision from its inception. In 1910, 1912 and 1914 (at its biennial conventions), it

67

urged calendar reform in three successive resolutions, each one stronger than its predecessor. In 1912 it sent an inquiry to Rome, asking for a clarification of the Vatican's attitude, and received the following reply from the Papal Secretary of State: "The Holy See declared that it made no objection but invited the civil powers to enter into an accord on the reform of the calendar, after which it would willingly grant its collaboration in so far as the matter affected religious feasts."

This reply was significant, in that it separated the civil calendar from the religious. The former was the responsibility of governments, the latter that of the churches.

The International Chamber's next action, in 1914, accepted the division of functions, and sought to obtain official action on an improved civil calendar. The Chamber (then the only existing top-level international agency) asked the Swiss Government to call a world conference to adopt a reform which already had received unanimous approval in the unofficial channels of the business and scientific world. Switzerland accepted the invitation, and was preparing the material for the conference when World War I intervened.

After the close of the war, in 1919, the International Astronomical Union revived the subject. It formed a committee under the distinguished chairmanship of Cardinal Mercier of Belgium. His leadership made the creation of this committee an event of world-wide importance. The Cardinal had just emerged from World War I as a triumphant symbol of resistance to tyranny. He was highly regarded as both scholar and leader in England and in America, as well as in continental Europe. His advocacy of calendar reform drew many Catholics into the movement, and also commanded the attention of the Church of England.

The Cardinal's committee spent three years on its scientific studies, which culminated in a conference held in Paris in 1922. The Cardinal subsequently resigned his presidential position because he felt himself not sufficiently equipped to deal with astronomical matters. A later meeting was held the same year in Rome, at which Professor Bigourdan of Belgium presided, with Abbé Chauve-Bertrand of the French Astronomical Society as secretary. The Abbé's interest in calendar reform continued to grow until he became one of the great Catholic leaders, highly influential by reason of his authoritative book, *La Question de Pâques et du Calendrier*.

At the Rome meeting, the Astronomical Union's "Commission 32" approved the perpetual 12-month equal quarter plan containing the one or two extra days and urged international adoption.

Science, government and business joined hands in the next stage of progress. The League of Nations was established in 1920, and was approached on the matter of an improved calendar in 1923. The Swiss Government, the International Chamber of Commerce and the International Astronomical Union all felt that calendar reform should have a place on the permanent agenda of the new international organization. Their suggestion was approved at Geneva, and the subject was allocated to the League's Section on Communications and Transit.

Now for the first time calendar reform was on an official basis in an international forum of governments. As an initial step, the League secretariat felt that it should clarify the division of authority between church and state—this seemed necessary because of pressure from several countries for stabilization of Easter, which obviously was an ecclesiastical matter. So a preliminary committee was appointed which included three ecclesiastical newcomers—the Reverend T. E. R. Phillips, secretary of the Royal Astronomical Society of London, representing the Archbishop of Canterbury; Professor Demetrius Eginitis of the Observatory of Athens, representing the Patriarch of the Eastern Orthodox Church, and Father Gianfrancheschi, president of the Vatican's Academy of Science, representing the Holy See.

The League of Nations, having confirmed through this group that the churches had no dogmatic objection to a reform of the civil calendar, proceeded to set up a "Special Committee of Enquiry" under the chairmanship of Professor W. J. M. Van Eysinga of the University of Leyden, Holland. Other members included the three ecclesiastical representatives, together with Professor M. G. Bigourdan, chairman of the International Astronomical Union's Committee on Calendar Reform, and Willis H. Booth of New York City, president of the International Chamber of Commerce. The committee was an excellent one, especially as the three ecclesiastical members were all scientists of high competence. Professor Van Eysinga was an enthusiastic advocate of calendar revision, with a thorough knowledge of the international situation and the need of unification in order to facilitate communications and mutual understanding.

The special committee continued its studies throughout 1924, 1925 and 1926, when it submitted its final report. There was complete agreement on the need for an improved calendar, but the committee members had been unable to reach a decision as to the legal steps by which this was to be brought about. They felt the need for a more urgent "mandate" from governments, and they suggested that "public opinion was not yet prepared to press for action." Accordingly, their chief practical recommendation was that all nations should be asked to set up committees to promote localized research. The ecclesiastical members of the committee added a formal statement reassuring the civil powers that "from the viewpoint of religious dogma the idea of calendar reform does not meet with difficulties of such a nature that they can be regarded as insuperable."

The vague statement that "public opinion was not prepared to press for action" seemed to call for explanation. Informally one of the committee members said: "We are convinced that this project needs a broader base of active support. We hope it can be obtained through the creation of national committees everywhere. *This does not mean that we expect calendar reform to be forced upon the League of Nations by an aroused public demand. That would be asking too much. In the past, reforms of this character have always been imposed from above. If they had to wait for public opinion to insist, they would never be realized.* This is historically supported by the records of the Julian, Constantinian and Gregorian reforms. Nevertheless, a certain preparation of the popular mind for calendar reform seems to us advisable and necessary." (italics mine.)

National committees were eventually created by many governments, but in some instances their membership was composed of minor officials, who failed to carry out important educational activities, and were not influential at home or in Geneva. Nevertheless, they served to accent the need for calendar revision.

In the United States an intensive campaign for calendar reform was conducted by George Eastman, the famous Kodak manufacturer. He had met with Moses Cotsworth of England, an ardent advocate of a 13-month plan who was successful in winning Mr. Eastman's support. A non-official committee, known as the International Fixed Calendar League, was formed in 1924 with headquarters in the United States, of which Mr. Eastman was the chairman. Mr. Cotsworth, director of the London office, was in charge of affairs in Europe. Although an able campaign was waged, it never gained the full interest and support of the people. It won mild approval among statisticians and the business world because of its *seeming simplicity,* but the public did not respond to a plan arranged on so awkward a number as 13 and which involved many unnecessary and drastic changes.

However, real interest in an improved calendar had been aroused in the United States, with the result that in 1928 and 1929 the House of Representatives introduced joint resolutions requesting the President to propose the calling of an international conference on calendar reform, or to accept, on behalf of the United States, an invitation to participate in such a conference. All this led up to the League of Nations calling the first international calendar conference ever recorded in history. It was held in Geneva, October 12, 1931, and lasted a week. It was the League of Nations Fourth General Conference on Communications and Transit that dealt with calendar reform.

A year before the international conference a new calendar organization had been formed in the United States, The World Calendar Association, advocating a revised 12-month calendar of equal quarters, with the perpetual feature originated by Abbé Marco Mastrofini. It conducted an intensive campaign, the purpose being to inform the people of the superior advantages of the 12-month revision.

One of its first activities was to approach approximately 50,000 Americans in various fields, obtaining in the first three months a membership of 2,500. A questionnaire, for example, was issued to the entire membership of the Chamber of Commerce in Wilmington, Delaware. Both the 13-month and the 12-month calendars were equally presented, resulting in the following interesting percentages: business opposing calendar revision 32.3 per cent, favoring the 13-month calendar 30.3 per cent, and favoring the 12-month plan 37.4 per cent. The newly formed organization was fully justified in the belief that, were full information given, the 12-month revision would unmistakably lead by a large majority. Further to advocate The World Calendar, a quarterly *Journal of Calendar Reform*—a compilation of calendar information—was initiated under the able editorship of the late Charles D. Morris.

In June 1931, a Preparatory Committee meeting was held in Geneva at which both the 13-month and the 12-month calendars were given a hearing, and both received a place on the agenda of the International Conference in October. The Preparatory Committee considered 187 plans and among those discarded were:

First, four long 35-day months and eight short 28-day months, "because the very perceptible inequality of the months would be extremely inconvenient from every point of view";

Second, a "Leap-Week Calendar" with an extra leap week every five, six, or eleven years would give three different lengths of years: 364, 371 and 378 days in order to keep the calendar in step with the seasons, rejected on the ground that it is "inferior to the existing calendar and cannot be considered at all";

Third, a decimal system;

Fourth, a five, six or ten-day week;

Fifth, plans for changing the date of the New Year to January 0 or a Monday or a seasonal point.

Dismissing these plans expedited the discussion for the October conference, for which three were chosen: the Philip's plan that regularized the months but omitted the perpetual feature, the 13-month plan and The World Calendar. The first was rejected because it was an insufficient reform, while there was an equal number of votes for the other two. The 13-month plan received the votes of Canada and Yugoslavia (who now support The World Calendar); and Switzerland and Greece approved the 12-month calendar of equal quarters. Both calendars contained the perpetual feature.

The conference considered the time "not ripe" and, religious opposition having been expressed by Orthodox Jewry and the Seventh-Day Adventists, the League resubmitted calendar reform to its member governments with the request that it be given further study and stressing the need for wider understanding.

In summarizing the result, the president of the conference, Mr. Vasconcellos of Portugal, reported that as far as reform was desired the *preference* was for a *per-*

petual calendar rather than for a mere regularization of the quarters (the Philip's plan).

Great interest was aroused in South America, where Dr. Ismael Gajardo Reyes of Chile organized, in 1934, the Latin-American Committee for The World Calendar. Through this committee, which represented the majority of the South American countries, he directed the activities of the national calendar reform organizations, and succeeded in winning the interest of a number of highly influential people—statesmen, priests and scholars. No bloc of national committees has been more powerful in the development of an international consciousness of the practical possibilities of calendar reform.

A noteworthy Labor Conference was held by the American States, members of the International Labor Organization, in Chile, January 1936. At the plenary session unanimous approval was given the following resolution: ". . . recommends the approval of the perpetual calendar of 12 months and equal quarters; and it resolves to request the Administrative Council of the International Labor Organization to send copies of this resolution to the Secretary General of the League of Nations, and to all the Governments of the American countries."

This action received subsequent approval by the International Labor Organization in Geneva, July of the same year. The result of this and the educational campaign by the Latin-American Committee, led Señor Don Agustin Edwards, representative of Chile on the League Council and his country's Ambassador to Great Britain, to submit in January 1937 a Draft Convention to the

League "requesting the adoption of the perpetual calendar of twelve months and equal quarters, known as The World Calendar," and declaring that this proposal "would be extremely convenient for commercial and business life and would enhance the welfare of the working classes, and would be very advantageous for all nations." The document further stated "the present Convention shall be ratified and the ratifications thereof shall be deposited with the Secretariat of the League of Nations not later than December 1, 1938." Here was a notable step, raising calendar reform to a higher level. The calendar was marching on.

The League submitted the Chilean proposal to its member and non-member nations and 45 replies were received. Of these 14 (later increased to 17) approved the Convention; 6 rejected; 8 made no observations, including the United States; 10 were unprepared, with Soviet Russia one of them; and 7 considered the time premature, among them being France and the United Kingdom. The League did not consider the result satisfactory and withdrew the item from the agenda. It stated, however, that it could "take up the question again if circumstances should, at a later date, be more favorable." This postponement proved unfortunate because two years later World War II prevented further action and thus ended all League participation. What the League had so enthusiastically begun, it failed to complete. Governments were not ready, they lacked the vision—"without vision the people perish." Although the League passed into oblivion, its seed bore fruit in the establishment of the United Nations organization.

It was in July, 1937, that I had the honor to be an

Associate Delegate of the American Delegation attending the Religious Conference of the Universal Christian Council for Life and Work, at Oxford. At the close of the conference, all the delegates were invited to a garden party at Lambeth Palace, London. As I was introduced to the Most Reverend Cosmo Gordon Lang, Archbishop of Canterbury, I was greeted with these words: "I hope our good friend Lord Desborough will live to see The World Calendar adopted, in which he so much believes." Such gracious words coming from the highest authority of the Anglican Church were indeed encouraging.

One of my cherished recollections was the warm friendship I enjoyed with Lord Desborough, father of calendar reform in England. Ever hospitable, one delightful incident occurred at a luncheon that he gave for His Excellency Don Agustin Edwards of Chile, Mr. C. David Stelling, chairman of the British Calendar Reform Committee, and myself at the Bath Club. He turned to me and said: "I shall call you Elisabeth, a name all England loves, that of her Queen and Princess." I was thrilled and impulsively exclaimed: "How very kind of you!"

Among many interviews with officials at the League of Nations, one comes vividly to mind. It was with M. Robert Haas, director of the Section on Communications and Transit, during which, in an annoyed manner he said: "Why must we deal with this calendar question, why wasn't it done long ago instead of bothering us now?"

I replied: "For the same reason, M. Haas, that you wish to do nothing about it, to leave it to the future, when again the same complaint that you are making will be made." He was taken aback, saying only: "Perhaps you are right." M. Haas died within a year and unfortunately the support he might have given The World Calendar was not possible.

The World Calendar Association, non-political, educational, free and independent in its activities, forged ahead. Many committees were formed throughout the world—South America, Europe and Asia—which laid the background that broadened it to an international association in 1947. The World Calendar Association, International, was thus prepared to work on a world basis with the newly established United Nations organization.

Peru, following the example of Chile, in 1947 submitted a resolution to the Fourth Session of the Economic and Social Council of the United Nations stating: "Whereas it is widely recognized that the present calendar is unsatisfactory for the economic, social, educational, scientific and other activities of man; that there exists a general desire to bring about its revision, and that the new calendar should have twelve months and equal quarters, be perpetually the same, with a stable pattern of quarter-years, months, weeks, days and fixed holidays. . . . That the Economic and Social Council appoint an ad-hoc Committee to study and pass judgment on the adoption of a new calendar on January 1, 1950."

Upon the recommendation of the president of the Council a *Note* was prepared by Trygve Lie, the Secretary-General of the United Nations, and distributed to the member governments. This *Note* is an important memorandum—a basic document for the approach of international action in the matter of calendar reform. It contains a most significant statement: "of all the drafts studied on the international plane, the draft [The World Calendar] submitted by Peru is the one which has received most favourable comments."

Hopes were high that at the Fifth Session of ECOSOC affirmative action would be taken. However, this did not happen. The proposal was dropped at the eleventh hour from the agenda. Other items appeared more important to the United Nations and were given priority.

Another opportunity was presented to The World Calendar Association two years later in 1949. Undaunted and convinced of the rightness of the cause, Panama, the little strategic country which geographically joins the North and South American continents, proposed the subject to the Fourth Regular Session of the United Nations General Assembly. Its representative, Dr. Ricardo J. Alfaro, presented a letter to the Secretary-General requesting that the subject be placed on the agenda of the Fourth Session. In the accompanying memorandum it was not only stated that "this perpetual calendar offers harmony and order to all strata of society" and that "millions of dollars annually would be saved," but that "the 365th day of the year in 'The World Calendar' is an international holiday, dedicated simultaneously in every country of the world to the universal harmony and unity of mankind, thus knitting all races, creeds, peoples and nations into a closer bond of fellowship, creating world-wide citizenship in the 'One World.' The potentialities of 'Worldsday' for strengthening and promoting international peace among all nations are of great value."

It is regrettable to record that the high plane on which calendar reform had now been placed was not recognized by the United Nations delegations in charge of the program committee. Again there was put forward the weak argument—"overcrowded agenda." (But when is an agenda not overcrowded?) The vote taken on the matter was 4 in behalf of the resolution, 4 against, 4 abstentions, with 2 absent. The vote lacked a majority, and the subject was automatically dropped from the agenda.

Meanwhile the Newspaper Advertising Executives Association had become interested and was instrumental in having The World Calendar introduced in joint bills in both houses of the United States 79th Congress, second session, 1946.

United Nations' failure to act in the matter, however, and the Orthodox Jewry and Seventh-Day Adventists injection once again of their own particular sectarian views in a civil calendar, clouded the issue. Subsequent bills in the 80th and 81st Congresses were permitted to "die in Committee"—they never reached the floor.

Another minor complication arose. A different 12-month revision had been introduced in Congress by the Hawaiian delegate, who presented the Edwards Perpetual Calendar. This plan differs from The World Calendar in that the extra day opens the year as "New Year's Day," presumably dated January 0, and Monday becomes January 1, with all subsequent weeks beginning with a Monday. The familiar order of the weekdays is thus disarranged, Friday becomes the 5th, Saturday the 6th and Sunday the 7th day of the week. These wholly unnecessary changes, and the beginning of every week on a commercial note, make the Edwards plan quite inferior to the superior World Calendar. It also "died in Committee."

Because of the negative stand taken by the United Nations, Congress did not take action. In the words of Senator Estes Kefauver, who introduced the bill in the first session of the 81st Congress (1949): "Should the United Nations General Assembly take favorable action, I am confident that the United States Senate's Foreign Relations Committee will report the bill out favorably, so that action can be taken on it in the Senate."

In 1953, India took the initiative by requesting Dag Hammarskjöld, the Secretary-General of the United Nations, to place World Calendar Reform on the 18th Session of the Economic and Social Council at Geneva, July 1954. In its transmittal letter, India stated: "The purpose of the plan is to adopt for the whole world . . . a new, fixed, uniform and invariable calendar, regulated astronomically according to the movement of the Earth around the Sun, and more regular, scientific and advantageous than the Gregorian Calendar." It proposed The World Calendar as "of great importance to the nations of the world," thus becoming a fervent sponsor.

During the course of the 1954 Geneva meetings of ECOSOC, the calendar revision movement received heartening support from the Vatican. On June 28 *L'Osservatore Romano,* the Vatican's official journal, featured a scholarly article on its front page, clarifying the Vatican's attitude toward calendar reform in general and referring to the Indian proposal in unmistakably sympathetic terms. The article stated: "The Church has no reason to oppose in principle a modification of the present Calendar. If there were a general desire for reform, motivated by serious requirements of the economic and social life of the peoples of the world, the Catholic

Church would not fail to consider the question, provided, naturally, that certain conditions which She Herself cannot overlook, are observed." Calendar revision is a civil matter, but this announcement is having a powerful effect upon large religious communities—both Catholic and non-Catholic—and upon governments as well.

Unanimous action was taken by ECOSOC at Geneva on July 28, 1954. The Secretary-General was requested to submit the Indian Resolution "and any other relevant documents to the governments of States Members and non-members of the United Nations, with the request that they study the problem and furnish their views by some time early in 1955." The Council also decided "to consider the matter again at its resumed nineteenth session [May 1955], together with the replies received from governments."

What does this mean?

It means that The World Calendar stands ready for the test. It means that every government must now stand up and be counted. It means that peoples the world over must also stand up and be counted, because governments hesitate to act without some expression from the people. Whether the United Nations will proceed in its work toward the successful conclusion of The World Calendar, depends upon the decision next May.

With favorable action by the United Nations and ratification by the respective nations, the most propitious time for adoption would be Sunday, January 1, 1961, when once again both the present calendar and The World Calendar share the same day, date, month and year.

What shall history record—a further postponement or

a forthright acknowledgment of the need and immediate action for improvement? When there is illness and the disease recognized, the cure is hastened. The calendar is ill and its cure should likewise be speedily effected.

X

DEVELOPMENTS IN ISRAEL

Day unto day uttereth speech, and
night unto night showeth knowledge.
—Psalm 19:2

TWO ANCIENT CALENDARS still influence our civilization, the Egyptian and the Jewish. Egypt gave us the solar seasonal year, establishing it on a sound astronomical basis which is the foundation of our present Gregorian system. The Jews gave us the week, with the deep spiritual satisfaction of a regular seventh day consecrated to rest and worship, now increasingly observed throughout the world.

The Jewish calendar in its entirety still survives among the Hebrew people and is the official civil system of the new State of Israel. Historically it is the result of a long series of revisions and adjustments, with important lessons for modern students of calendar reform.

The principal features of the Jewish calendar as it exists today are these: it reckons the years from 3761 B.C. (October 7 at 8:11 o'clock), a conventional starting point representing the Creation; it regards the day as beginning at sunset, which for convenience is reckoned to be 6 p.m., Standard Time (but in Jerusalem it is Jerusalem time, 2 hours and 21 minutes off Greenwich); the New Year comes in the autumn, either in late September or early October; the years consist of 12 months of alternating 29 and 30 days, with a 13th month inserted seven times in every 19 years; the Sabbath is observed at the end of the week, starting at sunset on Friday and continuing until sunset on Saturday, when a new week begins; until recently, the Jews had their own method of subdividing the hour into 1080 "parts" and each of these parts into 76 "moments"; the names of the months are of Mesopotamian origin and some of them perpetuate pagan deities.

The evolution of this calendar system has been intensively studied for many centuries, although the basic historical material is often fragmentary and incomplete. It is clear, however, that the earliest Jewish calendar was purely lunar, with 12 months of alternate 29 and 30 days. With advancing civilization came the need for putting the lunar calendar into a seasonal pattern. As with other ancient peoples, a 13th month was intercalated in various ways, often at the whim of rulers or religious leaders. Strangely, the Old Testament does not mention any intercalated month or its equivalent.

The months at first were numbered, but eventually they took on the Babylonian names, which they still bear today. The intercalated 13th month was taken over from the Babylonians but the method of inserting it and the order of the occasional 13-month years was a matter of slow and gradual development over a period of many centuries.

Actually, the present-day rule for inserting the 13th

month was not formulated until A.D. 358, when Rabbi Hillel II devised a permanent program on the basis of a 19-year cycle, wherein the seven years of 13 months are the 3rd, 6th, 8th, 11th, 14th, 17th and 19th. The thirteenth month follows the month of Adar and is called Veadar or Adar-Beth.

In current practice, the 12 "ordinary years" of the 19-year cycle may contain 353, 354 or 355 days, known respectively as common deficient, regular and abundant years, whereas the seven "leap years" may contain 383, 384 or 385 days, the embolismic deficient, regular and abundant years. Thus the Jewish years are of six different lengths.

In the days of Moses in *Exodus,* the year began in the spring month of Abib (subsequently called Nisan). This was changed later to autumn and the month of Tishri. In the period of the Patriarchs, the day began at sunrise. This was changed to sunset during the fourth century B.C.

Equally drastic changes occurred in the observance of the week. The early history of the Jewish Sabbath and the seven-day week is somewhat obscure. Predecessors of the ancient Jews (for example, the Chaldeans) considered the 7th, 14th, 21st and 28th days of the month as of ill omen, unsuitable for important enterprises, so that men feared to work on those days. The Hebrews observed these seventh days as days of rest, bestowing on them a spirit of sanctity and removing all associations with evil.

They added this conception to the Canaanite solar calendar which was in use by their neighbors, along with their own tribal festivals. But in that stage of civilization, calendars were not too definitely fixed or anchored.

Changes were made to fit emergencies, and the prevailing system could be freely altered.

It is significant that in the first 65 chapters of the Old Testament, periods of seven days are frequently noticed; but after the narrative of the Creation, no Sabbath is mentioned until the great religious leader Moses speaks to his people in the desert. Obviously there had been no strict adherence to the Sabbath observance in former times. Moses established the sacred seventh day and gave it emphasis as a preeminent feature of religious life and worship, which he strengthened further when he made it one of the Ten Commandments.

His first effort to fortify the Sabbath observance came, according to *Exodus,* as the result of the miraculous gift of manna from Heaven. The manna was gathered every day for five days and a double portion on the sixth day; then the Hebrews were commanded to rest and worship on the seventh day. In this manner Moses gave his people a dedicated Sabbath endowing it with divine authority.

During the Mosaic era, a radical change in the calendar came into effect. "Pentecontad" periods of 50 days were devised. Each period contained seven weeks of 49 days that included seven Sabbaths, with an extra 50th day as a special "offering to the Lord," always observed as the closing day of each pentecontad period. This calendar was in use in Palestine for many centuries.

It was at a much later date, during the Babylonian captivity, that the pentecontad plan with its special 50th day was abandoned and a regular *invariable* seventh-day Sabbath was introduced, with the Babylonian luni-solar calendar as its background and framework. At this time the Jewish religious leaders formulated their theory of the "unbroken continuity of the seven-day week," maintaining that their new system had started with the Creation and emphasizing the divine origin of the Sabbath. The Sabbath for the first time became identified with the idea of the unbroken continuity of the weeks. The simple, divinely inspired seventh day for worship was now confused with the new idea of the unbroken sequence of weeks.

"It was in the Exile," writes Dr. Harry Emerson Fosdick in his *Guide to Understanding the Bible,* "that the story of creation was brought to its climax in the admonition to keep the Sabbath, made sacred from the world's foundation. It was in the Exile that the laws were rewritten and codified stressing Jewish differentials."

Judaism from Babylon onward has maintained consistently its own religious calendar and its own particular concept of the unbroken continuity of the week. One of the foremost Jewish historians significantly points out, "The present Hebrew calendar is a direct heir of ancient Babylonia, just as the present Gregorian calendar is a direct heir of ancient Egypt."

MONTHS OF THE JEWISH YEAR

1 Tishri	30 days	7 Nisan	30 days
2 Heshvan	29 or 30 days	8 Iyar	29 days
3 Kislev	29 or 30 days	9 Sivan	30 days
4 Tebet	29 days	10 Tammuz	29 days
5 Shebat	30 days	11 Ab	30 days
6 Adar	29 or 30 days	12 Elul	29 days
Veadar or			
Adar-Beth	29 days		
(occurring only in leap years)			

353, 354 or 355 days in common years
383, 384 or 385 days in leap years

XI

REALM OF THE CRESCENT

I fear this iron yoke of outward conformity
hath left a slavish print upon our necks.

—John Milton

THREE HUNDRED MILLION Moham-
medans—concentrated in a dozen countries of the Middle East and adjacent parts of Asia and Africa—still use
a primitive lunar calendar that was adopted in Arabia
several years after the Prophet's death in A.D. 632.

Mohammed had no part in this calendar reform. It
was done by his *Companions* in an effort to carry out
what they thought was in his mind from their reading
of a single obscure passage in the Koran.

The pressing need for a Moslem calendar arose out of
the surprisingly rapid expansion of Mohammedanism
immediately after his death. In less than seven years the
tribesmen of Islam swept the decadent Roman Empire
out of Asia Minor and gained control of such remote
and renowned cities as Antioch and Damascus. Bound
together by a fighting creed, they developed a strong
conviction of invincibility. Their religious unity required formulation and stability.

To understand the background of their calendar, it should be remembered that Mohammed's public career was fairly brief: only 23 years elapsed between the day when he first appeared as a religious leader and the time of his death. His spiritual aim, as he stated, was a "restoration of the religion of Abraham," with emphasis on the unity of God and on the future life.

During his lifetime, the tribesmen around Mecca and Medina used a luni-solar calendar on the Hebrew pattern, in which a 13th month was intercalated every two or three years to adjust the lunar months to the seasons. Responsibility for the intercalation rested with a family of astronomers known as the Qalamas. The 13th month was placed at the end of the year.

The Arabs also steadfastly adhered to an ancient religious custom of observing four sacred months—the first, seventh and the last two months of every year. The intercalation of a 13th month between two sacred months (the last and the first months) brought about a great deal of disturbance. Should the intercalary month be observed as another sacred period? Or should it be regarded as an ordinary month and allowed to interrupt the religious observances?

Mohammed experienced all this confusion and, being solicitous for the spiritual and physical welfare of his people, he felt that the combination of intercalation and postponement led to error. It was a real tragedy to Islam that he did not live to clarify this situation. Possibly he was preparing to take up the calendar when death intervened.

Just before his death he proclaimed through a verse of the Koran: "Twelve months is the number of months ordained by God, according to God's book. . . . Any 'nassi' is the cause of confusion." Nobody knew exactly what the Prophet meant by the latter phrase. The word "nassi," translated by various authorities as *postponement, transferring* or *carry-over,* can hardly be translated as *intercalation.* But after him his *Companions* gave it that interpretation, and installed a purely lunar calendar.

Of course the "year" of twelve lunations and 354 or 355 days bears no relation whatever to the solar year. Therefore the Moslem lunar calendar wanders through the seasons and returns to its original position after a period of about 33 years. A Moslem who according to his calendar says he is 34 years old is actually only 33 years old by the Gregorian reckoning.

This purely lunar calendar led later generations of Moslems to strange dilemmas and inconsistencies, for the simple reason that while the lunar calendar may satisfy the requirements of the simple Bedouin living in desert isolation, it raises many difficulties when increased facilities of communication encouraged larger centers of population.

For example, a new moon may be seen by one clan and not by another living ten miles away: the next day therefore becomes the first day of the succeeding month for the first clan, while it remains the 30th day of the current month to the other.

In this connection the well-known writer, George Kent, tells a story which shows that even in the calendar there may be a story of adventure:

One day Jotham Johnson, of the University of Pennsylvania Museum, while crossing the Syrian Desert, beheld a troop of wild horsemen galloping down upon him and his party. All hands took firm hold of their rifles and prepared to make a stand.

The riders, however, had not come to rob or kill. All they wanted was a little calendar information. The night before had been cloudy and they clamored to be told whether the new moon had been seen at Deir, the town Johnson had come from. If it had, then Ramadan, the month of fasting, was over. If not, they would be obliged to stick it out for another 24 hours.

To remove this anomaly the intellectuals of later generations, when the influence of Islam expanded, found themselves between the meanings ascribed to the word of God on the one hand and the clearly ascertained laws of God on the other. They were forced to prescribe that the first month of each year, Muharram, should be assumed to have 30 days and the second month 29 days and so on alternately throughout the year, except for the last month which in 11 out of 30 years has 30 days instead of 29.

They implied that this assumption was to hold good irrespective of whether the moon was seen on the 29th or 30th, but they did not dare to clarify this implication because it would go against the prohibition of intercalation *ascribed* to the Koran.

But the orthodox saw through this implication and refused to accept the formula. For them the length of each month of the lunar calendar consisted of 29 *or* 30 days, not alternately, but depending upon whether or not two reliable men had *seen* the new moon on the evening of the 29th or 30th.

In recent years scholars have insisted that the interpretation forbidding intercalation is incorrect and that in all probability Mohammed intended the adoption of a twelve-month seasonal calendar of the type used by Rome and other Christian nations.

Whether Mohammed's immediate successors were right or wrong, they burdened all Islam with a strictly lunar calendar that has caused endless difficulties, sufferings and harassments.

One of the more important handicaps of the wandering calendar has been its effect on the annual Hajj or pilgrimage to Mecca. The rites of the Hajj, prescribing bare-headedness and the wearing of only two pieces of cloth, could only have been meant for a time of year when it was neither too hot in the day nor too cold at night. But, because the Hajj rotates in a lunar calendar through even the hottest and coldest months, thousands of pilgrims have suffered the rigors of the extreme climate of Saudi Arabia.

In 1953 the annual pilgrimage, always in the twelfth and last month of the year, came in midsummer. Ahmad Kamal, in the *Saturday Evening Post,* wrote that the heat ranged between 116 and 127 degrees, and on one day the mercury climbed to 142 degrees, causing the death of 4,411 pilgrims on that day alone. And all this tragic loss of life was due to the non-seasonal moon calendar!

"It is obvious," writes Mohammed Ajmal Khan, "that the Prophet wanted the Muslims to follow the custom of the Christians in the matter of the calendar, so that the Hajj should fall in the month of March—near the Christian Easter, the Jewish Passover, the Iranian Navroz and the Hindu festival of Holi. If this had been done, the Islamic message of peace and goodwill would have been better understood and there would have been no cru-

93

sades, no bloodshed in the name of religion, and no ill-will in the name of Islam."

Another well-known authority, Dr. Hashim Amir Ali of Osmania University, says: "And there *are* really only *twelve months in God's calendar* ever since the earth began to revolve around the sun in its present orbit. The two solstices and the two equinoxes divide the cycle of the year into four periods and in each of these a season begins, reaches its zenith and declines—making twelve sub-seasons in all. These may be called by any name one likes. The Koran merely emphasizes this fact in Nature—and man's incorporation of it in his calendars is a testimony of his attempts at abiding with God's creation."

These are matters which are of increasing concern to the Moslem religious authorities. But they do not fall within the province of the United Nations in its efforts to improve the present international *civil* calendar.

All Moslem countries use the Gregorian calendar in their international relationships. Its datings are widely employed in commerce, and most Arabic newspapers are double-dated. The Gregorian system is an alternative, generally recognized by law. The Moslem calendar is primarily for religious use; the Gregorian system is of course civil in its function.

No one at the United Nations has the remotest intention of touching in any way upon religious calendars, whether they be Christian, Jewish, Moslem or Hindu. Such changes, if they come at all, must be made by the properly constituted religious authorities.

The international civil calendar, however, is a matter on which all nations can agree. The Arab states are as interested as any others, in improving the present system,

94

to give it greater accuracy, utility and universality.

A statement from a Moslem representative of the government of India says: "The universal calendar proposed by The World Calendar Association is very useful indeed, and no religious question arises against its adoption. The lunar calendar was proposed for all the religious functions of Islam because its knowledge is possible for everyone naturally. Muslims will carry it on for their religious purposes, but for all other purposes and especially for government administration, the new reformed calendar should be adopted."

MONTHS OF THE MOHAMMEDAN YEAR

1	Muharram	30 days	7	Rajab	30 days
2	Safar	29 days	8	Shaban	29 days
3	Rabia I	30 days	9	Ramadan	30 days
4	Rabia II	29 days	10	Shawwal	29 days
5	Jumada I	30 days	11	Zu'lkadah	30 days
6	Jumada II	29 days	12	Zu'lhijjah	29 days*

* In leap year, 30 days

_____

354 or 355 days

XII

RUSSIA'S DIFFICULTIES

It is obvious that the eloquent demand of our century and of modern life will not stop before any difficulties, and therefore undoubtedly a practical solution of the calendar question is near.

—Leo Tolstoy

RUSSIAN CALENDAR HISTORY is no exception to that of other calendar histories of the past; it has been a varied one with many trials and errors. Eventually the Gregorian calendar was adopted by the government to conform with the greater number of other nations.

Dr. Vera Rossovskaja, astronomer of the Research Institute at Leningrad, wrote a notable book, *The Remote Past of the Calendar,* published in 1936, in which she stated that up to the end of the fifteenth century the Russian year began on March 1. Years were counted from the "creation of the world," an event that was placed in the year 5509 B.C. Then for a brief interval the Moscow government began the calendar year with September 1, until about A.D. 1700, when Peter the Great introduced January 1 as the beginning of the year, adopting at the same time the reckoning of the Christian era. This aroused the opposition of the Eastern Church.

In 1709 the calendar (the Julian calendar) was first

printed in Russia, more than 127 years after the Gregorian calendar had been introduced in Europe.

In the nineteenth century, because of the almost world-wide acceptance of the Gregorian calendar, the Department of Foreign Affairs used the Gregorian style in its relations with foreign countries; the commercial and naval fleets too were obliged to reckon time according to the Western calendar; and finally sciences, such as astronomy, meteorology, etc., which had a world character, were compelled to follow the new system. All this caused considerable complication.

In 1829 the Department of Public Instruction recommended a revision of the calendar to the Academy of Science. The Academy proceeded to petition the government to accept the Gregorian calendar. Prince Lieven, in submitting the plan to Tsar Nicholas I, denounced it as "premature, unnecessary, and likely to produce upheavals, and bewilderment of mind and conscience among the people." He further declared that "the advantage from a reform of this kind will be very small and immaterial, while the inconveniences and difficulties will be unavoidable and great." The Tsar, being apprehensive, wrote on the report: "The comments of Prince Lieven are accurate and just."

From thence onward frequent attempts were made to remove the ban, but to no avail. In 1918, after the Revolution, Lenin raised the question of calendar reform and, after an investigation of the subject, published a decree directing the adoption of the Gregorian style "for the purpose of being in harmony with all the civilized countries of the world."

The adoption of the Gregorian calendar necessitated

a cancellation of 13 days, instead of ten days, because in the interval three centurial years had been counted as leap years. Although the government officially accepted the Gregorian calendar, the Russian Eastern Orthodox Church still clung to the earlier and more familiar Julian. This is the reason, for example, that the observance of Christmas, on December 25 in the Gregorian calendar, comes in the Julian calendar on January 7.

In 1923, a radical change in the calendar took place. Soviet Russia abolished both the Julian calendar, used by the Russian Orthodox Church, and the official Gregorian calendar that had been installed by Lenin. A new calendar was introduced, in which the weeks were changed and all religious feasts and holy days were replaced by five national public holidays associated with the Revolution.

The "Eternal Calendar" went into effect on October 6 (Revolution Day), giving five days to the weeks and six weeks to the months, so that there were 12 months of 30 days, plus five holidays with national names instead of weekday names. The chief objective of the "Eternal Calendar" was to increase production, and special color cards indicating the day of rest were distributed to the workers. Rest-days became staggered. It was not realized at the time that such an arrangement would cause real hardship to family life. After several years of trial, in 1931, the five-day week and staggered rest-days were replaced by another system.

This new plan provided for a 12-month year with the same holidays as before and the same extra day for leap years, but a new week of six days was introduced wherein the rest-day came regularly on the 6th, 12th,

18th, 24th and 30th of the month, in addition to the five national holidays.

Through all these changes decreed by the Russian government, the Church still clung to the Julian calendar, and farmers and peasants continued to work and plan according to the seasons, months and weeks, as had their forefathers.

To historians and statisticians these various calendar changes bring real difficulties. Reference to the Russian Julian calendar must be made previous to 1918, from 1918 to 1923 the Gregorian calendar was in use, from 1923 to 1931 the five-day Russian Revolutionary calendar must be consulted, and from 1931 until 1940 the Russian calendar with the six-day week was in effect. From 1940 onward, official Russia returned to the Gregorian calendar with its seven-day week, using Sunday as a rest-day. By this latest action the government returned to the idea of Lenin, and Russia is once more using the same calendar as "all the civilized countries of the world."

Leo Gruliow, editor of *The Current Digest of the Soviet Press,* recently wrote: "A combination of factors appears to have swung Russia into the growing list of supporters of calendar reform. Whether the Soviet will go beyond its present cautious endorsement of study of The World Calendar Association proposal remains to be seen. That the development of the Russian studies will lead to beneficial results is definitely assured."

XIII
INDIA'S CONFUSIONS

*Men look to the East for the dawning things,
for the light of the rising sun.*
—Douglas Malloch

CALENDAR REFORM took a major step forward when India declared itself in favor of it. Initiated in Europe, developed and advanced in the Americas, it has now, through India's action, expanded to include Asia. Thus three vast areas—Europe, the Americas and Asia—are all contributing to give the world a better idea of unity and cooperation by establishing one and the same time chart—The World Calendar.

Rudyard Kipling, born in India and familiar with her peoples and customs, wrote:

Oh, East is East, and West is West, and never the twain shall
    meet . . .
But there is neither East nor West, Border, nor Breed, nor
    Birth,
When two strong men stand face to face, though they come
    from the ends of the earth!

The bonds of better understanding and friendlier relationships between the East and West were thus greatly strengthened by India in recognizing two strong forces

—Time and the Calendar—uniting the Eastern and Western Hemispheres. Time, we know, is the great healer; the Calendar can become the great uniter. Historians may well acclaim India's activity in calendar reform one of the most notable events of the twentieth century.

India's interest in this subject is easily understood since her own calendar situation is "chaotic and intolerable." The government must print every year an official almanac containing four different calendars, including among these the Gregorian and Mohammedan; this enormous compilation consists of 3,273 pages; astrological practices and countless religious doctrines complicate recording of days, months and years; conflict exists between scientific astronomy and "fantastic astrology"; the calendar lacks a scientific basis on which to obtain accurate calculations and data; India has no national observatory; lunar calendars increase difficulties; the 1,400-year-old rule relating to the seasons and the lengths of solar months causes wrong calculations and the lengths of solar months followed by the almanac makers violate the laws of scientific astronomy.

The following solutions have been suggested by Professor M. N. Saha, chairman of the Calendar Reform Committee of India:

Establish an Indian Greenwich, where annual compilations can be made; Ephemerides, Nautical and Air Almanacs can be printed; a national civil calendar can be instituted; the calendar should be based on the perpetual solar time reckoning for the whole of India; lunar calendars should be avoided for all civil purposes; length of the year should be 365.2422 days; present irregular months should be replaced with the length of months as proposed in The World Calendar; and days should be calculated in the accepted astronomical manner, from midnight to midnight of Indian Greenwich.

The two "strong men," or powerful forces—Time and the Calendar—are fulfilling Kipling's prophecy. There will be no longer a cleavage between "border, breed nor birth," on the subject of Time when The World Calendar becomes the universal measurer of Time on Earth.

India's action before the United Nations and her official calendar committee, both undertaken with the sanction of Prime Minister Nehru, are lifting calendar reform to a high international position, particularly as the subject is non-political, non-partisan, non-nationalistic and non-sectarian.

The opinions of Prime Minister Nehru were impressively stated some time ago in regard to bettering general conditions:

The past brings us many gifts: indeed, all that we have today of culture, civilization, science or knowledge of some aspects of the truth, is a gift of the distant or recent past to us. It is right that we acknowledge our obligation to the past. But the past does not exhaust our duty or obligation. We owe a duty to the future also, and perhaps that obligation is even greater than the one we owe to the past. For the past is passed and done with, we cannot change it; the future is yet to come, and perhaps we may be able to shape it a little. . . .

It has been said that the adoption of the solar calendar by the Egyptians marked a great cultural achievement. It can rightly be said that modern calendar reform—The World Calendar—sparked by India's active participation, will mark a significant step in establishing greater world unity and cooperation.

XIV

THIRTEEN'S RISE AND FALL

Thou art weighed in the balances, and art found wanting.
—Daniel 5:27

THE FIRST known proposal for a 13-month fixed calendar came from a colonial American in 1745 and was published in the *Gentleman's Magazine* of London under the guise of "Hirossa Ap-Iccum." Later in *Scott's Magazine* a "Mr. Urban" of Maryland also wrote an essay on a 13-month perpetual calendar.

Toward the middle of the nineteenth century, the French mathematician and philosopher, Auguste Comte, proposed another 13-month calendar which he belabored with innumerable names of great men in history. Such cumbersome naming of days, weeks, months, invited its failure from the outset.

It was not until many years later, in the early part of the twentieth century, that Moses B. Cotsworth actively advocated and zealously worked for the 13-month calendar. Cotsworth, the modern "father of the 13-month calendar," was born in York, England, where he was brought up by his grandparents who used the old shadow-pin, noon-mark and hour-glass methods, knowledge of which facilitated his later researches. His business training began with the North Eastern Railway Company, where he showed special aptitude for making calculations and investigations which brought him the commission to make extensive computations and adjustments in revising the British Railway rates during 1891-1895. In recognition of his talents he was called upon to establish improved systems of railway statistics, which were adopted by the British Railway Companies and the Ministry of Transport.

This experience brought him into direct contact with the defects of the Gregorian calendar and the resultant difficulties with which every statistician must wrestle. He resented the many hours and the labor lost in adjusting accounts on such a haphazard and wandering system of tabulation. Dealing strictly with figures, the 13-month calendar with its fixed months, each of 28 days and four weeks, appealed to him as the ideal solution. In his campaign for this plan he won the active support of the American business man and philanthropist, George Eastman, founder of the Eastman Kodak Company, who financed the campaign during his life.

Mr. Cotsworth's plan was simple. All the months of the calendar were given 28 days each, divided into four weeks, beginning with Sunday and ending with Saturday, with the 13th month inserted between June and July, called "Sol." With this established, the 364-day year was given an extra day with the suggested name "Year Day" in common years that would account for the 365th day, and "Leap Day" in leap years that was added in the midyear, which would be the 366th day.

These days, besides having their own names, also had their special dates, December 29 in common years and June 29 in leap years. He proposed that these extra days be observed as holidays.

The advantages of the plan were as follows: Each month had the same number of working days and the same number of weeks; each month was comparable with all the other months; each week would be one quarter of the month; dates for public meetings, law court sessions and other pending events would always be fixed; the end of each month would coincide with the end of the week. It was a system especially designed for statisticians.

This plan, however, had grievous drawbacks: The seasons were ignored; quarter years could no longer approximate seasons by months, as each quarter would have 3 months plus one week or $3\frac{1}{4}$ months; as fractions are always complicated, the ultimate result would be the blotting out of months and the reduction of the calendar to mathematical groupings of days and weeks by numbers; it would become an incredibly dull and monotonous routine; there would be thirteen monthly closings in the payment of bills, which would increase bookkeeping with attending expense; thirteen monthly rentals and thirteen monthly bills would add to the cost of living; the conversion of dates (as only the first 28 days would agree with 28 days of the Gregorian calendar) would bring innumerable difficulties; the remaining 337 days would all undergo change, nullifying past records and hampering research.

The 13-month plan would standardize the month to the point of rigid monotony and the calendar would lose its pleasing variety. Nature expresses infinite variety with order and does not conform to rigid patterns, as seen in her different seasons, climates, winds, and directions.

Mr. Cotsworth in his plan succeeded in bringing the calendar to the ultimate point of simplicity. However, the French astronomer Camille Flammarion has said, "such simplicity that falls into monotony is not adaptable to human life."

When the League of Nations submitted a plan in 1937 to its member and non-member states, the selection was the Draft Convention of the Chilean government, which requested adoption of the perpetual 12-month year of equal quarters. The 13-month plan was thereby definitely dropped.

The thirteen-month advocates in the United States counted heavily upon winning American support by capitalizing on the number thirteen, so closely associated with the early history of their country. This reminds me of an interesting incident.

It was during the meeting of the Preparatory Committee that I first met Meredith N. Stiles, the American Secretary of the International Fixed Calendar League, which supported the 13-month plan in the United States. At an informal luncheon Mr. Stiles complimented The World Calendar Association on the admirable pamphlet it had issued several months previously, and confessed to a difficult nut that he had to crack in one of the arguments made against the 13-month plan. He referred to the following statement:

The thirteen-month calendar enthusiasts point exultingly to the early history of the United States and declare that "Thirteen is not unlucky." They admonish us not to worry about Friday, the thirteenth. It may have been a matter of chance or an unrevealed divine motive that gave America her original thirteen colonies. We do not know. In commemorating this historical fact, the flag was fashioned with thirteen stripes to represent the original thirteen States, and the artist who designed the Government seal hid within its motif many thirteens. Today, however, the United States of America is made up of 48 States—*four times twelve*—which fact is symbolized by the 48 stars in her flag. As a matter of sentiment, therefore, America as a nation ought to respond more strongly to a twelve-month calendar plan than to a thirteen-month calendar proposition. By so doing we honor the past with the thirteen stripes in the flag yet recognize the present with the 48 stars. Our history is a clear indication that the thirteen influence carried an incompleteness— a beginning. In view of this fact, do we want to substitute an incomplete calendar, the future of which is so problematical? We have at hand the choice of an improved plan, The World Calendar, its structure of twelve months having survived through aeons of time. Is not that a better guarantee?

He then continued, "But, Miss Achelis, I have found the answer; you have made a mistake. The United States has four territories—Hawaii, Puerto Rico, Alaska, and the Philippines—and these sum up to 52 and not 48. Your argument is therefore faulty." I replied, "But there is a difference between states and territories, and *52 weeks* in your 13-month calendar are the same as in The World Calendar; there exists no disagreement there." My reply was greeted with hearty laughter, Charles D. Morris exclaiming: "Stiles, you cannot get the best of Miss Achelis." It was an amusing incident, but it showed the friendly spirit that existed between us, although we each fought valiantly for our own plan.

In the League of Nations report of 1931, a suggestion was made that, while the present calendar was in effect and to ease somewhat the difficult situation for statisticians and controllers, an auxiliary calendar, such as a 13-period system, could be used as a stop-gap. After carefully studying this proposal, I wrote in the *Journal of Calendar Reform:* "Legalizing auxiliary calendars would complicate not simplify the calendar. . . . To invite their increase or to give them 'official character' would seem unwise to most governments."

But the idea of an auxiliary calendar was not abandoned. During the difficult war years the United States Budget Department revised its pay system on 13 periods of four weeks. All federal employees are now paid on a fortnightly system, a scheme which sacrifices the conveniences of the conventional monthly system. Thus the government uses a dual calendar: one for its budget and accounting departments while the present calendar is retained for all other uses nationally and internationally.

Since the Federal government would benefit from the stabilized World Calendar both in its 26 yearly pay-roll system and its regular *monthly and quarter-year* accounting procedures, it is surprising that the United States delegation at the United Nations did not favor calendar reform, "being satisfied with the present calendar." It was also stated that calendar reform "was a purely domestic matter."

This raises the question whether the United States delegate was informed of his own government's dual calendar system. If not, it would appear that the welfare and convenience of the citizen were insufficiently considered as well as the unnecessary expenses and confusions which the present calendar imposes on every one.

An auxiliary fiscal calendar of whatever kind or any specialization is not the solution.

The opinion of the United States government, fortunately, is not world wide and should not prevent acceptance of a better proposal by other governments.

The 13-month calendar and the 13 periods of four weeks have been weighed in the balance and found wanting.

THIRTEEN-MONTH CALENDAR

S	M	T	W	T	F	S
1	2	3	4	5	6	7
8	9	10	11	12	13	14
15	16	17	18	19	20	21
22	23	24	25	26	27	28

Year Day, December 29   Leap Day, June 29

XV

WORLD CALENDAR REFORM

The times are big with tidings.
—Robert Southey

IT IS INCREASINGLY apparent when dealing with so universal a subject as the calendar that personal, political, national and religious bias should have no part. Like the sun which shines upon the inhabitants of Earth, calendar revision affects all the peoples of the world, whether of the East, West, North or South. The point of view must be global and must consider the common good of all, not any particular major or minor group. The revision must be approached with the perspective that the subject requires. By adhering to this simple principle, confusion and difficulties are avoided.

My interest in calendar reform began in the summer of 1929 while I was staying at the Lake Placid Club, New York. I heard Dr. Melvil Dewey, founder and president, give a lecture, "How To Simplify Life." He closed his talk with a strong plea to improve the calendar which, in its many irregularities, was far from satisfactory. He then advocated a 13-month calendar that disturbed me. How could a non-divisible number like 13 simplify?

A fortnight later, on Sunday September 8, the *New York Times* published a letter by the engineer Lewis E. Ashbaugh of Denver, Colorado, in which he opposed the perpetual 13-month plan and advocated the more easily divisible perpetual 12-month calendar favored in Europe. He wrote: "While we are planning an improved calendar, let us also insist on the very best, with all conditions considered, and let us adopt the revised twelve month year of equal quarters and equal working-day months, easily adapted from the calendar we now use."

The letter instantly attracted my attention and as I was reading, I heard a clear voice saying: *"You must work for this plan."* It was so real, I had to obey, for here was a call that had to be followed. It has ever been a reassuring force sustaining me in the work and convincing me that this plan comes from a higher power.

The World Calendar is solar wherein everything fits, everything agrees, everything is stable. Based on a purely scientific and mathematical principle, its purpose is to meet the social, scientific, cultural and international requirements of the day. Religious feast days and national holidays have their regular places, but these are separate and distinct and do not affect its ordered arrangement.

The revised 12-month calendar accepts the perpetual feature of the Roman Catholic priest Marco Mastrofini who considered the year as of 364 days, wherein the 52 weeks (each of seven days) fit within the year.

The 365th day or the 1/7 of a week, that indispensable fraction, is placed at the end of December as a day set apart between two weeks whereby the familiar order of the week is not interrupted. This last day of the year has the name Worldsday and the specific date December

W, which corresponds to December 31. It belongs to the annual sequence of days—Saturday, Worldsday that is followed by Sunday, the first day of each new year. By this method every outgoing year is securely sealed with the new Worldsday holiday and the year becomes a finished time period.

The annual "year book," fully completed in its cycle and observed with proper celebration on the year-end Worldsday, is then placed on the archive shelves of Time, where it can be referred to whenever desired. By this method the year is no longer tied to a day of the first week of an incoming year. A new year book is ever ready to be opened on New Year's Day Sunday, January 1.

The 366th day in leap years is likewise placed between two weeks in the midyear after Saturday, June 30, and before Sunday, July 1. Its name is Leapyear Day and its date is June W or June 31. In this manner the new Worldsday (365th day) every year and the new Leapyear Day (366th day) every four years keep the calendar equalized, balanced and perpetual. These new stabilizing days are unique in the calendar in being universally observed as *world holidays*.

The method of the extra day can be compared to an interesting Chinese fable.

A farmer, at his death, left 11 sheep to his three sons, with instructions that the eldest should have one-half the number of sheep, the second son one-quarter and the third son two-thirds of the remainder. This strange division greatly perplexed the family until a wise mathematician showed them a way of solving their problem. He told them to go to a neighbor and borrow a sheep.

With this borrowed sheep, the sons now had 12 animals which they could distribute in accordance with the wish of their venerable father. The eldest son received one-half the number, or six sheep; the second son received one-quarter, or three sheep; the youngest received two-thirds of the remainder, or two sheep. When the borrowed animal had thus served its purpose, the sons returned it to its owner.

In reverse, calendar reformers have solved their problem by *withholding* the 365th day, whereby the year has 364 days, a number easily divisible into equal quarter years of 91 days each and equal half years of 182 days each. With this satisfactory solution, the 365th day is returned to the calendar and placed at the end of the fourth or last quarter of the year as the new Worldsday.

The perpetual World Calendar retains the twelve months and divides these into equal quarter and half years. Each quarter year is given 3 months with the lengths more evenly apportioned. The first month has 31 days and begins with a Sunday, the following two months have 30 days each and begin respectively with a Wednesday and a Friday. Every month has 26 weekdays plus Sundays. Each quarter year begins with Sunday and ends with Saturday, has 91 days, 13 weeks or 3 months approximating a season. Corresponding days and dates always agree and perfect coordination is had among the different time units, resulting in accurate comparability from year to year. Every year begins with Sunday, January 1, and ends with the non-working new world holiday—Worldsday. Holidays can be stabilized according to the customs of the various nations. Likewise, religious feast and fast days are anchored to their regular days and dates and celebrated in keeping with the various religious faiths.

It is noteworthy that the *first* day of every year, every week and every quarter year begins on a Sunday and that the *seventh* day of every year, every week and every quarter year ends on a Saturday. For the first time in calendar history, the week will actually have its regular place in the calendar and will no longer impose the objectionable shifting of weekdays and dates as heretofore.

Only six months, between the 28th of February and the 1st of September, are changed by one or two days. From the 1st of September through the 28th of February, the calendar remains the same as the Gregorian.

The dates which call for change are three—March 31, May 31 and August 31—replaced by three new ones—February 29 and 30 and April 31. This will call for a minor adjustment of days which were observed on the vanishing dates. Birthdays will now be observed on the day before, on the 30th of the month, the method used by leap-year children ever since 1236—over 718 years ago when King Henry III of England decreed that the leap day should be "reckoned in the same month wherein it groweth and that day, and the day next going before, shall be accounted for one day." For the first time in calendar history the *day* of birth will be honored with the *date*.

The World Calendar is a mathematical masterpiece. It deals as successfully with the arbitrary numbers 7 and 13 as with the easy numbers 2, 3, 4, 6 and 12. And with the aid of the one or two stabilizing days the calendar at long last becomes a steady and reliable time system.

Not only is arithmetical order inherent in this plan, but it achieves as well the most difficult quality of all—simplicity—with just consideration to all the various parts. And in this mathematical arrangement the quarter years are identical without in any way interfering with the independent and different seasons. There also exists a pleasing variety within the three months of every quarter year.

The late Dr. Samuel Boggs, geographer for 30 years with the Department of State, wrote: "Every one can carry a perpetual calendar in his head that is good for all time after the new system goes into effect. This derives from the fact that every quarter of the year is alike, for every year, so far as the days of the week are concerned. The trick is so simple that a child can learn and apply it, with pleasure and convenience for the rest of his life."

In its ordered stability The World Calendar—silent, steadfast, serene—is a pathfinder to peace.

It is most interesting to note that this new calendar follows the Biblical pattern of the symbolic holy city of Jerusalem, based on a foursquare plan. It has three *months* or "gates" to every quarter year, twelve months to every year. The leaves of the tree of life within the city are for the "healing of the nations" which in The World Calendar are the new *world holidays* that in their international observance will foster greater unity among the nations.

The foursquare principle is particularly unique to our planet Earth, which is influenced by the four seasons, the four winds, the four cardinal points of the compass and the four elements—fire, water, air and earth.

Every individual, too, functions on the four basic planes of life; namely, spirit, soul, mind and body.

The ideal of the square is far more significant and important than is generally recognized. The American form of government is based on the principle of the square—the executive, the legislative, the judicial and the citizenry—each respected in its own right.

The business world presents the same picture. It takes the cooperation of four groups—management, production, distribution and consumer—to make a profitable business.

In the educational field the grammar and high schools, college and university complete the pursuit of learning. And interestingly enough, simple arithmetic has its four distinct processes—addition, subtraction, multiplication and division.

There are also four definite measurements—length, height, breadth and thickness—and Dr. Albert Einstein has taught us to think in terms of four dimensions instead of three.

No higher praise is given man than "to be on the square," which would be well indeed for mankind to recognize in all his many and varied activities.

Reverting to the previously described temperamental calendar family with which we are burdened today, we now learn to our relief that with a few important rearrangements it has become a harmonious calendar family wherein all the various members have each their rightful place. The *Day-child* is happy because it knows exactly how many days it has for play and work; the *Week-child* has learned discipline, running in and out of months at regular intervals; the *Month-child* enjoys its

FIRST QUARTER

JANUARY	FEBRUARY	MARCH
S M T W T F S	S M T W T F S	S M T W T F S
1 2 3 4 5 6 7		1 2
8 9 10 11 12 13 14	5 6 7 8 9 10 11	3 4 5 6 7 8 9
15 16 17 18 19 20 21	12 13 14 15 16 17 18	10 11 12 13 14 15 16
22 23 24 25 26 27 28	19 20 21 22 23 24 25	17 18 19 20 21 22 23
29 30 31	26 27 28 29 30	24 25 26 27 28 29 30

← ★ WORLDSDAY, December W

FOURTH QUARTER — OCTOBER NOVEMBER DECEMBER

SECOND QUARTER — APRIL MAY JUNE

THE WORLD CALENDAR

of

TWELVE MONTHS

and

EQUAL QUARTERS

★★ LEAP YEAR DAY, June W →

THIRD QUARTER

SEPTEMBER	AUGUST	JULY
S M T W T F S	S M T W T F S	S M T W T F S
1 2	1 2 3 4	1 2 3 4 5 6 7
3 4 5 6 7 8 9	5 6 7 8 9 10 11	8 9 10 11 12 13 14
10 11 12 13 14 15 16	12 13 14 15 16 17 18	15 16 17 18 19 20 21
17 18 19 20 21 22 23	19 20 21 22 23 24 25	22 23 24 25 26 27 28
24 25 26 27 28 29 30	26 27 28 29 30	29 30 31

larger room at the beginning of every quarter because of the five Sundays, after which it moves into smaller rooms during the two shorter months, each of equal dimensions; and the *Quarter-year child* and the *Half-year child* are justly regarded.

This outstanding achievement cannot be credited to any one particular nation or person. It is a progressive development to which many minds have contributed. Valuable historical facts have been explored, and increasing knowledge and understanding have been acquired. The calendar has at last become a world measurement of Time—a universal world chart for all humanity to use and enjoy.

For instance, in a large corporation the tabulating and analyzing of the various statistical reports, essential in the evaluation of the business, are easily made because of the perfect coordination of the different time units. One department deals with the day, another with weekly or bi-monthly payments, then there are the monthly salaries and the seasonal and quarterly reports to be considered, all of which coordinate in every quarter, half year and the year itself.

In every business and industry and in all the professions, a perpetual ordered calendar will facilitate methods of calculating time as well as simplify book-keeping.

Interest payments, insurance premiums and rentals will be based on regular schedules, an advantage to both sides of the transaction.

With this perpetual calendar in use, days and dates always agree; planning for sports events and vacations is facilitated; transportation and college schedules remain stable from year to year; there will always be 52 Mondays, no more and no less, and that applies as well to the other days in the week.

Birthdays and anniversaries will be recorded on the *day* of occurrence as well as date, month and year. The day will no longer be the forgotten time unit; it has come into its own. According to an old English rhyme, I am a Saturday child who "works hard for a living," but I shall never be able to record this weekday of my birth because in The World Calendar I shall become a Tuesday child "full of grace."

Holidays will be fixed in this new standardized calendar. This will benefit the employer in production and management since wandering holidays will no longer interfere with his activities; nor will the worker and employer lose out by closing plants and other places of business because of marooned working days.

From the practical point of view wages on the extra day inserted between two weeks will be paid at the usual time and a half holiday rate. The additional cost is fully compensated by the many savings effected by The World Calendar. New Year holidays will no longer range over seven days. They will no longer fall on a Sunday, to be celebrated the day following. The new Worldsday and Leapyear Day holidays will always be observed on the day *before* Sunday. Thus Monday, January 2, will be the first business day of every new year and Monday, July 2, the first business day of the second half of each quadrennial year.

A fixed Labor Day in America on its regular day and date, Monday, September 4, is of inestimable advantage to educational institutions, eliminating costly expenses of preparing and printing new catalogues every year.

It will do away with the guesswork of finding out on what date the first Tuesday after the first Monday in November will fall—always November 7.

Calendar makers like clock makers will continue to flourish notwithstanding the fact that the dial on the clock and the lay-out of the calendar do not change. Diaries, notebooks, engagement pads, and calendars which show the phases of the moon, call for annual printing. There will always be a demand for different designs and in different material.

A study at the University of Illinois states that "the arrangement of a scholastic calendar affects many outside interests—boarding houses, restaurants, merchants, booksellers and publishers, telephone and telegraph services, railroads and airlines, hospitals and doctors.

"What we need is a time plan that will be every year the same. We need it, not only for ourselves, but for our dealings with other educational institutions, where correlation is highly important. The ideal situation would be for all schools in the nation (and even in the world) to be on a time plan which would be an almost unchanging photostat of dates, a universal blueprint of all educational and scholastic activities.

"Thus the proposed World Calendar offers not merely financial savings, but other advantages of paramount value—whereby accomplishments will be easier, errors less likely, conflicts more avoidable, double-treading and backtracking unnecessary. The economies in operation will provide a vast reservoir of improved service to those whom we educators seek to serve. The man-hours which will be saved are beyond calculation, and the benefits will be reflected in teaching, research and efficiency."

These advantages, and many others, are the result of the perfect coordination of the different time units in The World Calendar.

In the past, as we have noted, the reform of the calendar was in the hands of rulers—a Caesar, a Constantine, a Pope. Today, man has progressed to a broader concept and understanding of the calendar, and realizes that the revision is international, lying beyond national confines, political bias, religious sectarianism, racial distinction and individual influence. The World Calendar rests not upon one or two governments for approval, but on international action and decision of the greater number of nations in which, through the United Nations, the people have a voice.

Above all, the perpetual World Calendar conserves our most valuable commodity—Time. It was Benjamin Franklin who admonished Americans, "Do not squander time, for that's the stuff life is made of."

To achieve these desirable objectives certain outmoded customs and traditions must be abandoned. There must be a willingness to cease thinking of today in terms of yesterday and make today stand for a better tomorrow. Sectarian, self-centered, narrow thinking must give way to wider universal fields of thought. Horizons must expand beyond the confines of group prejudice.

In these days unity is particularly vital and it is incumbent upon nations, governments and the public to encourage systems wherein an interrelationship of greater understanding, harmony and good will is advanced. The World Calendar is an outstanding example of this ideal. Certainly it bears tidings of great moment—One World Calendar for One World.

THE WORLD CALENDAR

January	31 days	July	31 days
February	30 days	August	30 days
March	30 days	September	30 days
April	31 days	October	31 days
May	30 days	November	30 days
June	30 days	December	30 days

Annual Worldsday December W or 31
Quadrennial Leapyear Day June W or 31

XVI
WORLD HOLIDAYS

*. . . and the leaves of the tree
were for the healing of the nations.*
—Revelation 22:2

£VERY CALENDAR CHANGE in the past carried a unique feature. The Egyptians introduced the solar year of twelve months with 30 days to each month, closing it with five additional days so as to conform to the seasonal year. The Julian reform accepted the leap-year day. The Constantinian contribution was the week of seven days and the first day Sunday as the official day for Christian worship. The Gregorian harnessed the calendar to the seasons from which it had strayed, by cancelling ten days from the calendar and amending the leap-year rule.

The new feature of The World Calendar is the "Worldsday," which takes the fractional 1/7 day of the week (the 365th day of the year) and places it at the end of every year as a *world holiday*. By this method every year is stabilized and comparable with the other years—the annual day of prayer and praise, of brotherhood and good will.

Similarly the essential 366th day in leap years, the

"Leapyear Day," another *world holiday,* is placed be-tween the last week of the second quarter and the first week of the third quarter whereby the calendar keeps its balance—a day of joy and recreation, of play and sport, of friendly comradeship with one and all.

It is unhappy to note that opposition has been ex-pressed to these unique and beneficial world holidays on the ground that they will create two eight-day weeks—one at the end of every year and another in the middle of the calendar in leap years. These days, according to Orthodox rabbinical Jewry and Seventh-Day Adventists, will cause wandering Sabbaths. Do they not realize, how-ever, that travelers who cross the International Date Line unfailingly experience either an eight-day or a six-day week, depending on the direction taken? When Asia-bound the week is short and has but six days, when America-bound the week is lengthened to eight days. Here are instances when the "unbroken continuity" of weeks is invariably broken.

Moreover, in the present Gregorian calendar the week constantly wanders throughout the year. Every new year is compelled to begin on a different weekday so that the first date, January 1, may fall on any one of the seven days. This grievous fault of wandering weeks The World Calender corrects. With the new Worldsday in effect, every year will actually begin on the first day of the week, Sunday, and on the first day of the first month, January, and likewise the Sabbath will always be the seventh day of the week and of every new year. The cal-endar becomes a stable instrument of Time for man-kind's daily use, enhanced by the new world holidays, forming a rainbow bridge of many colors whereon peoples of all climes, customs and faiths meet in a spirit of increasing understanding and fellowship.

It is not in emphasizing opposition but in highlighting agreement that the success of reforms and forward-looking ideas depends. Civilization and man cannot stand still. To grow and to live man must have vision to forge ahead.

Resistance to Moses was temporary, for the Ten Commandments have survived through the ages, transforming man from a savage to a civilized human being.

Opposition to the healing by Jesus of Nazareth on Sabbath days brought forth his immortal words: "The Sabbath was made for man, not man for the Sabbath." There is no one today who would not heal, who would not assist anyone in distress because the day was a Sabbath.

Opposition to Paul and the disciples gave rise to the eternal truth: "The letter of the law killeth, the spirit giveth life." He warned not to make the law a stumbling stone.

Likewise opposition to The World Calendar because of the two inspiring world holidays will be shortlived. The antagonism of certain religious sects cannot prevail. "There is one thing stronger than all the armies of the world, and that is an idea whose time has come."

Worldsday and Leapyear Day in their universal observance will bring peoples and nations closer together and awaken in them a keener awareness of man's interdependence and interrelationship, and the increasing need for cooperation and unity. This is the *idealism* and the *realism* inherent in The World Calendar—a Calendar for Today and Tomorrow.

In this brief discourse on the calendar and its effect on civilization, an oustanding lesson is clear. It must be freed from shackles of sectarian belief, superstition, tradition and narrow, restricting prejudice. Only as the calendar emerges and is built on scientific, astronomical, mathematical and spiritual ground can it freely serve humanity and the entire world.

It is well to recall the wise words of an American Congressman, Senator Karl E. Mundt (then a Representative), when introducing his bill on The World Calendar, July 15, 1946: "Time, and the calendar as a standard of time, are the property of all and belong to every person. No party, no race, no religion, and no organization can claim a vested right or ask preferential treatment at the expense of the majority. In our democratic nation the greater good for the greater number must prevail."

On the matter of religious holidays and feast days, these indubitably rest with religious leaders.

An outstanding calendar authority, Professor Martin P. Nilsson, in his scholarly book, *Primitive Time-Reckoning*, writes in his concluding sentence that time-reckoning must be emancipated "from the fetters of religious cult."

The World Calendar, civil in scope and purpose, free from narrow sectarianism and based on astronomical grounds, achieves the regular flow of seasons, days and years. Notwithstanding trial and error and growth through the centuries, the calendar keeps to the original concept of Time as designed by the Creator.

XVII
SET IT RIGHT

Our time is out of joint; but O delight,
That we are born this day to set it right!

IN THE LONG STRETCH of six thousand and two hundred years since the first solar calendar was given to civilization by the Egyptians, only four changes have been made—a remarkable record, testifying to our calendar's essential soundness.

But today modern discovery, invention, and economic and social developments, linking the peoples of the earth closely together, call for another revision. In meeting this challenge, our century, like that of the ancient Egyptians, may well be remembered for its historic contribution to calendar evolution.

The young United Nations has wisely taken the first step to set the calendar aright. In the unanimously approved Resolution, adopted in the 18th session of its Economic and Social Council in Geneva, Switzerland, Secretary-General Dag Hammarskjöld was requested to ask the governments of the world, both States Members and non-members of the United Nations, to express their views early in 1955.

In the past, customs and practices were established by the edict of a sovereign, prophet or pope. Today authority is vested largely in governments and their peoples. Since governments must now stand up and be counted on the matter of calendar revision, the immediate task of peoples—of every one of us—is to urge upon their respective governments the vital need for a stable and ordered calendar and the manifold benefits it will have upon our civilization, opening doors for greater potentialities.

With a substantial number of governments approving an international study to be undertaken by the United Nations, preparations can be made for The World Calendar to be put into effect on Sunday, January 1, 1961, the earliest moment after 1956 when the present and proposed calendars share the same day, date, month and year.

Ample time is thus provided for making the transition smoothly, for avoiding the abrupt and disruptive difficulties that occurred, as we have seen, when the Julian and Gregorian reforms were first put into operation. No gain of days as in the Julian transition or loss of days as in the Gregorian change will occur. The present calendar will merge easily into the new system with Saturday, December 31, 1960, of the current calendar being followed with Sunday, January 1, 1961, of The World Calendar.

Few achievements can bring greater satisfaction than this to our generation. We shall have heeded Prime Minister Nehru's words, "The future is yet to come, and perhaps we may be able to shape it a little." Like the grain of mustard, our "little" will branch in many directions, encircling the earth, becoming universal. With The World Calendar in use man's days will become more orderly, harmonious, equitable and stable.

Dr. Robert Norwood, the late eminent minister of St. Bartholomew's Church in New York City, invited me to his study one afternoon to enquire about the progress of The World Calendar in which he was an ardent believer. Toward the end of our talk, he looked me squarely in the eye, saying, "Elisabeth, should you fail—which I do not believe you will—remember this, you have registered on the side of right."

Unforgettable words, living words—"on the side of right"—and those other unforgettable, living words of Gandhi: "I welcome the international movement for calendar reform . . . which will help to unify the peoples of the world."

Because it is scientifically, socially and spiritually right, The World Calendar will become an accepted part of the pattern of our lives. When that not too distant day comes, we shall all wonder that so much time, labor and thought were necessary to secure adoption of a reform so simple in plan, so magnificent in purpose.

I long to have this generation—all of my fellowmen in whatever land—raise their voices and give their hands to the cause of The World Calendar. It belongs to all men alike, a calendar of the people, for the people, by the people and *with* the people. Leaders in the governments of the world, charged with its universal adoption, urgently need the assurance of their people's support.

We are all God's children and He has revealed to us His concept of the calendar in the divine command to regulate the orderly succession of times and seasons, of days and years. It is the responsibility of each of us to contribute to the fulfillment of the practical ideal of The World Calendar for One World.

THE WORLD CALENDAR

	S	M	T	W	T	F	S
JANUARY	1	2	3	4	5	6	7
APRIL	8	9	10	11	12	13	14
JULY	15	16	17	18	19	20	21
OCTOBER	22	23	24	25	26	27	28
	29	30	31				

	S	M	T	W	T	F	S
FEBRUARY				1	2	3	4
MAY	5	6	7	8	9	10	11
AUGUST	12	13	14	15	16	17	18
NOVEMBER	19	20	21	22	23	24	25
	26	27	28	29	30		

	S	M	T	W	T	F	S
MARCH						1	2
JUNE	3	4	5	6	7	8	9
SEPTEMBER	10	11	12	13	14	15	16
DECEMBER	17	18	19	20	21	22	23
	24	25	26	27	28	29	30 w

W—Worldsday (a world holiday)—equals December 31 (365th day) and follows December 30 every year.

W—Leapyear Day (another world holiday)—equals June 31 and follows June 30 in leap years.

INDEX

The World

JANUARY

S	M	T	W	T	F	S
1	2	3	4	5	6	7
8	9	10	11	12	13	14
15	16	17	18	19	20	21
22	23	24	25	26	27	28
29	30	31				

FEBRUARY

S	M	T	W	T	F	S
			1	2	3	4
5	6	7	8	9	10	11
12	13	14	15	16	17	18
19	20	21	22	23	24	25
26	27	28	29	30		

MARCH

S	M	T	W	T	F	S
					1	2
3	4	5	6	7	8	9
10	11	12	13	14	15	16
17	18	19	20	21	22	23
24	25	26	27	28	29	30

SECOND QUARTER

APRIL

S	M	T	W	T	F	S
1	2	3	4	5	6	7
8	9	10	11	12	13	14
15	16	17	18	19	20	21
22	23	24	25	26	27	28
29	30	31				

MAY

S	M	T	W	T	F	S
			1	2	3	4
5	6	7	8	9	10	11
12	13	14	15	16	17	18
19	20	21	22	23	24	25
26	27	28	29	30		

JUNE

S	M	T	W	T	F	S
					1	2
3	4	5	6	7	8	9
10	11	12	13	14	15	16
17	18	19	20	21	22	23
24	25	26	27	28	29	30

W—Leapyear Day (another world holiday)—equals a June 31 and follows June 30 in leap years.